Praise f

"Angie Choi approached her cancer diagnosis as an opportunity for healing, digging deep into the physical nature of the disease and its treatment while also honoring insights into her human nature that nourished her spiritually. Through this synergy, she repaired and rebuilt the balance she needed to thrive. Through her narrative, she shares in intimate detail the steps she took as she moved along this intensely personal path to healing. There are gems here for every reader!"

— Miriam Kalamian, EdM, MS, CNS
Author of *Keto for Cancer: Ketogenic Metabolic Therapy as a Targeted Nutritional Strategy*

"Dr. Angie Choi provides a detailed report on how she used non-toxic metabolic therapy for managing her ovarian cancer. She was able to translate scientific information from published clinical and preclinical studies into a logical and effective treatment strategy for managing her cancer. The scientific and spiritual stress management strategies she employed are presented in clear language and, when followed, will give hope to cancer patients for improving their quality of life and overall survival."

— Thomas N. Seyfried, PhD
Professor and Author of *Cancer as a Metabolic Disease: On the Origin, Management and Prevention of Cancer*

Whole New Me

*Healing From Cancer
in Body, Mind, and Spirit*

Angie N Choi, EdD

Kosmos Publications Website: https://kosmospublications.com

Kosmos Publications, LLC
2803 Kavanaugh Blvd., #250049
Little Rock, AR 72205

Edited by Matthew Gilbert

Library of Congress Control Number: 2022923621

First Edition

ISBN: 978-0-9752663-3-5

10 9 8 7 6 5 4 3 2 1   22
Printed in the United States of America.

This book is dedicated to all those

whose lives have been changed by cancer.

May we let the light inside illuminate the way out of darkness.

Dedicated to my parents and my spiritual teacher,

the lights of my life, who showed me what support truly is.

ALSO BY ANGIE N CHOI

My Dreams: A Simple Guide to Dream Interpretation

ISBN 978-0-9752663-0-4 (paperback)

ISBN 978-0-9752663-1-1 (epub)

Contents

Figures

Introduction

Healing means to make whole. The etymology of the word comes from the Old English *hælan* which means "to make whole or sound" as well as "to cure or save."[1] We often think of healing as curing an illness or fixing a wound, but the root meaning indicates *wholeness*, which means an essential state of integrity. In my healing experience from cancer, I realized that it was Wholeness (also known as Oneness, Pure Love, Consciousness) that heals all diseases, and that the integration of body, mind, and spirit facilitates healing on all levels of being (physical, mental, and spiritual). My healing process from cancer did not just occur in the body but also in the mind and soul. Cancer also didn't happen all at once but unfolded gradually as it developed. No one suddenly gets cancer; it evolves over time through physical, mental, and environmental conditions. The fundamental insight I had about healing is that we are *already* Whole, but we forget that and start thinking and behaving as if we are not. We erroneously believe that we are not complete and think of ourselves as fragmented, broken, not enough, or separate (the *other*) which leads to living in ignorance of our completeness. This grand illusion creates imbalance which then leads to conditions that produce disease, but when we start the journey back to Wholeness, we can heal.

When I thought about how to organize this book, I wondered how to convey my healing process because it wasn't completely chronological or linear. Reflecting on how cancer occurred at the physical level, I could look backward for earlier signs of health issues, but mental and spiritual imbalances were not as easy to pinpoint in linear time. Healing from cancer was more cyclical and layered —like a planetary body having its annual return. More apt metaphors to describe my healing process would be a helix or a spiral staircase—endless strands or segments that are essentially part of a larger whole. Also, I wanted to convey that healing was not just horizontal but also vertical; it occurs in all planes of being similar to how slicing an onion reveals all its connected layers. I finally decided on using three main chapters to organize my healing process: body, mind, and spirit with some thematic overlap as all these aspects of being are interconnected.

Introduction

I wrote this book because I wanted to share my experience of cancer from these three perspectives. Most cancer biographies focus on the physical aspects of cancer, and I realized that a more holistic narrative on cancer— especially with an Indian philosophical foundation— was missing. To fully explain my cancer experience, the appendices include brief, introductory definitions of the material, mental, and spiritual dimensions of being as seen through the lens of Indian spiritual traditions. Although there are other traditions that view a human being as an integrated self with body, mind, and spirit; my background is in Indian philosophies or spiritual traditions, and that is why they are presented here. In particular, I present the process of manifestation, the difference between mind and Consciousness, what intuition is, and the healing potential within the spiritual plane of being.

My intention is not to write a book on Indian philosophies but to include them to the extent necessary to convey my experience. I also tried to make these philosophical concepts as clear and succinct as possible without delving too deeply into them. For readers who want to explore Indian philosophies further, many wonderful sources are available.[2-5] I suspect that most readers, especially those with cancer, will be most interested in the physical chapter (the body) of this book, but I encourage you to be open to the philosophical ideas presented in the mind and spirit chapters of this book even if they are contrary to your own. This book is not intended to change anyone's beliefs but to provide the background for *my* experience. Additionally, without understanding how the mind comes into creation from an Indian spiritual perspective, it will be difficult to comprehend what the mind actually is in relation to Consciousness. Mind and consciousness are used interchangeably in common parlance, but they are actually distinct. Unless you're a philosopher, you may never have even pondered this difference, so I ask the reader to peruse the explanations presented in the appendices, especially if they aren't familiar.

I also need to explain the various terms for Consciousness that will be used interchangeably throughout this book: Awareness, Oneness, Wholeness, Observer, Seer, and Spirit. They are capitalized to indicate their eternal, unchanging reality as opposed to phenomena that change (impermanence). Consciousness is often thought of as "the mind," but based on my personal experience with meditation, my spiritual teacher's instruction, and my study of Indian philosophies—specifically Samkhya, Yoga, Tantra, and Vedanta—I propose it is far more than that. Consciousness is the actual seat of Awareness, and the mind is an instrument or faculty that allows us to interact with our external and internal environments.

I wrote the kind of personal, holistic story about

cancer that I wanted to read and that would have helped me while experiencing it. My sincere wish is that this book may be useful to anyone who is living with cancer, healing from illness in general, or approaching health through an integrated lens.

Angie N Choi, EdD
Little Rock, AR
August 8, 2022

Chapter 1: The Body

When I was first diagnosed with ovarian cancer in 2021, it was a fluke. Like many people, I learned about my cancer diagnosis from testing for a totally different health issue. In my case, it was for back pain. Before delving into this diagnostic thunderbolt, let me go back to early signs that my body was ill. Retrospectively, I see that the signs of imbalance were evident back in 2014, seven years prior to my diagnosis, and perhaps even earlier. I had been a strict vegetarian for over a decade at that point and been vitamin B12 deficient for some time. Years of working indoors, sitting in front of a computer screen, also led to low levels of vitamin D. Though the role of micronutrient (vitamin and mineral) deficiencies in the development of cancer is complex, studies have indicated potential cocarcinogenic effects and associations.[1-3] During this time, I started noticing a slight burning sensation in my stomach. I had a gut feeling that it could be something called an H. pylori (Helicobacter pylori) infection. I knew that East Asians had the world's highest rates of H. pylori and stomach cancer,[4] and even though I grew up in the U.S., I thought I should get tested for the bacteria just in case.

In 2005, Barry Marshall and Robin Warren were awarded the Nobel prize in Physiology for discovering H. pylori and its role in gastritis and ulcers. Marshall had used himself as a guinea pig and drank a concoction of H. pylori brew. He then developed an H. pylori infection which proved that it was a pathogen that led to gastritis, ulcers, and stomach cancer. Prior to their research, it was uncertain if bacteria could survive the highly acidic environment of the stomach.[5] I also had a family history of stomach cancer and gastric issues, and I'd had a particularly bad case of traveler's diarrhea several years prior. I got tested that year, and as suspected, I was diagnosed with an active H. pylori infection.

These spiral-shaped bacteria grow in the mucosal layer of the stomach.[6] They damage stomach tissue and cause inflammation that leads to stomach ulcers and cancer. H. pylori bacteria weaken the stomach lining by secreting an enzyme called urease which makes stomach acids more neutral and creates a hospitable environment for the bacteria.

When the lining is intact, we are protected from feeling the acids that digest food. I had been having occasional stomach pain, a sign that my stomach lining had been compromised. After testing highly positive for H. pylori, I started the standard cocktail of a proton pump inhibitor and antibiotics: omeprazole, clarithromycin, and amoxicillin. Later, I retested with a breath test, and the results were negative. I also requested an esophagogastroduodenoscopy (EGD) to examine the esophagus, stomach, and small intestinal linings. The results came back normal with no evidence of esophagitis (inflammation of the esophagus), stomach ulcers (open sores in stomach lining), tumors (abnormal growth of tissue), or erythematous mucosae (redness or irritation in the digestive mucosa). The duodenum (first section of small intestine) also appeared to be normal. I continued to get H. pylori tests thereafter on a yearly basis. H. pylori is one of those persistent bacteria that is difficult to eradicate completely, so annual testing should be performed. All my results came back negative. Everything was looking good.

Then, in 2017, I was meditating and had an intuition about cancer. This was the first time I had heard the word *cancer* internally. I wasn't sure if the intuition was about me or someone else. Intuition had often told me when someone was ill or dying, but it wasn't always clear for who unless it came attached with a name. (See Appendix D for further discussion of intuition.) Initially, I thought that

H. pylori had come back and was creating a precancerous environment in the intestinal lining, so I got another EGD. This time, the results came back as positive for intestinal metaplasia, a precancerous change in the lining of the stomach with an increased risk of cancer. So not cancer but on its way. Rather than using conventional medicine again, I decided to take an Ayurvedic approach to healing my stomach using herbal supplements in powder form because of my sensitive microbiome. I wasn't keen on taking more antibiotics since repeated administration causes antibiotic resistance in addition to side effects. In 2018, I contacted an Ayurvedic practitioner who had been trained by Vasant Lad at the Ayurvedic Institute in New Mexico. I respected Dr. Lad's knowledge immensely having previously read his books. These Ayurvedic consultations helped me heal the stomach lining and rebalance the microbiome. I had always had regular bowel movements, but I could see that I wasn't fully digesting food in my stool. After taking the herbs, my bowel movements occurred more easily than before, and the stools were soft and smooth (a type 4 on the Bristol scale).[7] My overall wellness and immunity improved as well through the application of Ayurvedic medicated oils using self-administered lymphatic massage.[8]

Ayurveda, which means "the science of life" in Sanskrit, is an ancient medical system that is over 5,000 years old.[9] Ayurveda views a human as an energetic being with a matrix of energy flowing through body, mind, and spirit. Wellness occurs when this flow is harmonious through all levels, and disease occurs when this energy is out of balance. In Ayurveda, *prana*, a subtle lifeforce energy, pervades both the dense level of the body and the subtle level of the mind, so healing the physical body can also affect the mind and vice versa. After taking the herbs for three months, test results were negative for H. pylori, and another EGD pathology report in 2019 indicated that the metaplasia had healed. The esophagus, stomach, and small intestine mucosa were normal.

During these years from 2017–2019, my stress levels were high as my brother had been diagnosed with pancreatic cancer and died within a year of the diagnosis. He lived in Atlanta, and my elderly parents and I travelled there several times during the last year of his life. It was difficult to witness his suffering, but the love and support of his community was deeply moving. My sister-in-law, a nurse by profession, had advocated and cared for him with fierce devotion, and there was a distinct spiritual feeling of love that was palpable in their house amidst the stream of people coming to say goodbye.

Simultaneously, my elderly father who lived in Little Rock was suffering from prostate cancer, edema (swelling), constipation, and weakness. He had trouble urinating due to scarring in the urethra from prostate procedures and had to have a suprapubic catheter put in.[10] That was when life with a leg bag started. Never a big water drinker, my father would get urinary stones that blocked his catheter a few days after it was replaced; urine would collect and create pressure on his bladder. This made him feel like he had to go to the bathroom constantly until we could get the catheter changed out. The problem was, he was weak and a fall risk so getting up to go to the bathroom was dicey. This became extremely challenging and more so as we were all travelling back and forth to Atlanta, but his son was dying, and he needed to see him as much as he could before he passed.

On one such occasion, my parents and I sat in the back of the plane close to the bathroom. I was worried about flying with my father because I never knew when his bag would clog up, and he also needed assistance in the bathroom. We had gotten his bag changed out a few days before, so I was hoping we would have a clog-free trip. But shortly after take-off, the back and forth to the bathroom started. We were on a small plane, so I couldn't fit in the bathroom with him and had to stand outside the door. After doing this a few times, I sat down in my seat and waited for him to come out. I looked out the window for a few minutes and then saw my father walking down the aisle with his pants down by his ankles as passengers looked on. Our trip had just begun! This glimpse gives a sense of our daily challenges during that time. The last time we went to Atlanta was for my brother's memorial service, and I believe this deeply affected my father, even though he didn't show it outwardly. By this point, he had already retreated inwardly, was hardly speaking, stopped wearing his hearing aid, and spent most of his time in bed.

Having been a vibrant, energetic character who ran Mr. Cool, a local iconic clothing store, until his early 80s, my father quickly lost his energy after retiring and soon needed daily care and assistance. My elderly mother took care of him as best as she could with me as relief, but we realized that we needed help. Even though I felt spiritually elevated when helping my parents, all the doctor's appointments, administrative responsibilities, house maintenance, and driving back and forth while still working full time was exhausting both physically and mentally. A short while later, we received home hospice assistance so my father and mother could get some help at home. Even though I had been a hospice volunteer in California in the 1990s, I didn't know that an individual could get hospice services for not being able to do the activities of daily living. I had assumed that a patient had to be terminal with six months or less to live. (Little did I know that my father would pass away within six months.) Between hospice, home help aides, my mother, and myself, we were able to string together 24-hour home care and supervision. Looking back, I am comforted by the fact that my father was able to stay in his home until he passed away peacefully in his bed. Still, the year 2018 was especially stressful as both my brother and father died. I did not fully realize the impact of such high stress levels during that time and how it affected me as well.

Taking Care of Mom

After my father passed away, I was concerned about my mother living on her own. Thankfully, she had wonderful neighbors who watched out for her. Over the years, she had tended her yard—an acre of land—but it was too much to maintain despite her insistence to the contrary. She and I both wanted her to move closer to me, so we started house hunting. We looked at many houses close to mine, but we kept wishing that we could live next door to one another. Then, through the support of the universe, my lovely neighbors, who empathized with our situation, decided to sell their house to us. That is when the moving and renovation project began. My parents had lived in their house for over 40 years, so packing it up, clearing it out, holding garage sales, and making charity donations took their toll. I went over there after work and every weekend until everything was finished. Simultaneously, I was getting the new house prepared and renovated for my mother to move in. There were many projects to oversee: new carpet, paint, a deck expansion—all while getting another EGD to check my stomach. I was also planning a three-week vacation to Korea for my mother's 80th birthday and putting together the details for each day of our trip. I was exhausted! A month after my mother moved in, we left for Korea and took my father's ashes back to his hometown. We also went to my mother's hometown and stayed with my aunt. My uncle had hurt his back terribly and was confined to a hospital bed. We visited him a few times while there, and I am so thankful we were able to spend time with him as he died a few months later. The trip was healing for my mother and me. Feelings of familial love and connection after losing my brother and father palliated our loss.

A few months after we returned, my mother developed excruciating head pain that did not go away. This was not a normal headache or even a migraine, so I called 911 and got her admitted to the emergency room. A computed tomography (CT) scan revealed she had an aneurysm and that blood had pooled in the front of her brain. She needed to undergo a procedure where a thin catheter is inserted in the groin through blood vessels until it reaches the brain. Tiny platinum coils are then inserted to essentially plug up the aneurysm from the main artery, so it doesn't rupture.[11] She was in the intensive care unit (ICU) for 10 days and then admitted to a hospital room. This happened right before COVID-19 broke out in the U.S., so I was able to stay in the ICU with her. Although I am grateful for the wonderful care she received, being in an ICU for ten days was miserable because the staff woke her up every two hours to make sure she was cognizant and that her brain was working properly. It is not hyperbole to state that it may have been one of the most stressful experiences of our lives not to be able to sleep for more than two hours for ten days! Once I got my mother home, she needed 24-hour care and supervision, so I moved in with her for a month and took medical leave from work to care for her. Speech, physical, and occupational therapists also came by to help. She gradually recovered and gained her strength back, and after another month, she was back to being mostly independent. Again, I was exhausted.

In retrospect, I realize that those three years were extremely stressful both physically and emotionally. I knew I was stressed but didn't realize how constant and impactful it was. Stress affects multiple physiological systems. When we are faced with a threat, we experience fear in the amygdala in the medial temporal lobe of the brain. This initiates a coordinated defensive response between the autonomic, neuroendocrine, musculoskeletal, and information-processing systems in the body to fight, flee, or freeze.[12] Our breathing suddenly changes, blood vessels dilate to direct more blood to the heart and muscles, and the hypothalamus-pituitary-adrenal (HPA) axis initiates secretion of cortisol to fuel our muscles.[13] Any dysfunction within this physiological orchestration, whether under or over-activated, can disrupt our equilibrium and lead to disharmony.[14] Stress can be both positive (*eustress*, like planning a vacation) or negative (*distress*, like losing a loved one). Stress can also be short-term, intermittent, or long-term. When it's short-term, our physiological systems can regain homeostasis, but long-term stress exceeds our ability to cope. Chronic stress makes us more susceptible to digestive issues, inflammation, and conditions that feed malignant tumors.[15] It also increases angiogenesis and metastasis—growth and spread—of cancer cells.[16] Stress is not the only factor in cancer development, but it does play a key role in the deterioration of the terrain.[17] I now realize that chronic stress, exhaustion, a compromised microbiome, increased inflammation, and elevated levels of glucose from my diet all contributed to the growth of cancer in my body.

In January 2020, the Center for Disease Control (CDC) confirmed the first laboratory-confirmed cases of COVID-19 in the United States.[18] It took about another year for an emergency use authorized (EUA) vaccine to become available. The distribution of the vaccine was rolled out in waves to health care workers, seniors over 65, and front-line educators. I received my first dose in January 2021 early one morning, and by that evening, strong abdominal cramps had begun. Prior to getting the vaccine, I was concerned about side effects because my body was sensitive to medications, vaccines, and environmental toxins. When the cramps started, I didn't panic, thinking I was either having a strong reaction to the vaccination or had contracted COVID and my immune system was recognizing it. Subsequent COVID tests indicated negative results for the virus, though. The next day, I had chills and the worst abdominal cramps of my life! All I could do was lie in bed all day. Looking back after my cancer diagnosis, I wondered if the Pfizer mRNA vaccine had somehow stimulated my immune system to recognize the cancerous cells with an unintended immunotherapeutic effect?[19] I was also coming off a three-day fast right before I received the first vaccine, which also likely boosted my immune system.[20] I had no major effects after the second dose. Several months later, however, the abdominal cramps returned, but this time there was no obvious external cause. I had not had any recent vaccinations or food poisoning. Still, I knew something was off internally and I was growing more concerned. I was about to discover just how ill I was, but I never would have thought that realization would come from an orthopedic visit for back pain.

Unexpected Test Results

Earlier that year in February, a particularly heavy snowfall befell Arkansas. I shoveled out the driveway so my elderly neighbor's home health aides could park there as she needed 24-hour care. Two weeks later, I woke up in the morning and could barely move or get out of bed from intense back pain and sciatica shooting down my legs. I had never experienced this type of pain before. For the next few days, I tried to get by with heating and cooling pads and lying down, but the pain was not going away. I went to see an orthopedist, who took X-rays that indicated the spine and bones looked healthy. She said that I probably had a pinched nerve, and that rest, time, and physical therapy would help with the pain. She was mostly right; after about 6 months, my pain level went down from 10 to about 2, but I still had sciatica pain while standing up. It was painful enough that I couldn't stand for more than a few minutes without needing to sit down. The lingering sciatica, combined with the return of the abdominal cramps, motivated me to get more tests done.

I decided to address the sciatica first and went back to my orthopedist to request a magnetic resonance imaging (MRI) scan. Diagnostic tests have to be ordered by physicians and approved by health insurance companies before they will pay for them. My orthopedist agreed to request the lumbar spine MRI, and it was scheduled for the following week. I was hoping the MRI would provide a more nuanced look at possible causes of the sciatica. I thought it would show spinal stenosis—a narrowing of the space in the spine—because I felt relief from sciatica when bending forward or sitting down. When I accessed my online electronic health records to view the MRI results prior to my follow-up with the orthopedist, the last thing I expected was a diagnosis of a large tumor! The results indicated a large tumor of 15x17x1 centimeters: the size of a cantaloupe. When I first read the results, I was shocked. Here is a portion of the results exactly as was written.

> Myomatous uterus. Incompletely imaged heterogeneous signal intensity large mass in the pelvis towering above the level of the umbilicus with areas of postcontrast enhancement along the posteroinferior aspect. This appears to be displacing the urinary bladder anteroinferiorly without a distinct fat plane between the two structures. While this may represent a large degenerate fibroid (given that there are other leiomyomas in the uterus), a dedicated contrast enhanced MR examination of the pelvis is recommended for further evaluation. Possibility of an ovarian pathology would also require exclusion.

The first thing I did was search for *myomatous uterus*. To my initial relief, it indicated that the mass seemed to be a benign leiomyoma—a smooth muscle tumor in the uterus—that was likely non-cancerous. Then, I recalled that the dimensions were quite large, and it was alarming to think I had such a large mass in my uterus. I had not had any pain in my reproductive organs, so how had this happened without noticing it! I felt relieved, though, because as long as it wasn't cancer, I could deal with whatever would come next. At this point, I had never had an MRI nor was I experienced with diagnostic imaging reports, so I was optimistic that it was likely benign. I did not really dwell on the last sentence of the report: "Possibility of an ovarian pathology would also require exclusion."

When I had my follow-up, the orthopedist ordered another MRI to look specifically at the pelvic area since the first scan was lumbar and not nuanced enough to provide clear details of the tumor. She also informed me that while she could order the second MRI, she was not a gynecologist, which is who I would need to see going forward.

Two images from the initial MRI illustrating inferior and lateral views of the tumor are shown in Figure 1. The large white sac, seen more clearly on the left, is the tumor. The lateral image on the right shows how far the pelvis protrudes due to the tumor's size.

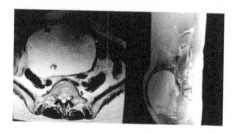

Figure 1. MRI Tumor Images

Likely Origins of My Tumor

Before proceeding, let me backtrack to the years that

the tumor likely developed. I had noticed a pelvic pooch forming under my belly button for a few years starting around the time of my transition from perimenopause to menopause (age 47–50), but I thought it was just fat. My hormonal balance had shifted during that time, resulting in weight gain, enlarged breasts, and occasional hot flashes. I was going to the bathroom more frequently than before, but I figured that was a result of aging. I did not notice any significant mood changes or depression other than grief from losing my loved ones. During this period, I was eating a high carbohydrate diet—all organic, but still high carb: basmati rice, lentils, beans, whole wheat bread, fruit jams, dairy, cheese, and honey. I often ate large amounts of fruit all at once; eight mini mandarins or a pound of grapes were nothing to me. And even though I felt full, I was also snacking on chips, chocolate, and ice cream after meals while watching online videos. I wasn't taking blood sugar levels with a glucometer during this time, but I'm sure my levels were high. I was definitely prediabetic and perhaps insulin resistant and diabetic as well. I felt uncomfortable going to bed because the food had not fully digested— sometimes not even by the next morning! I shudder to think how much glucose was circulating in my blood throughout the night from post-dinner snacking. Elevated levels of "fasting blood glucose" (blood sugar levels after an 8-hour fast) are associated with cancer risk as sugar is the primary fuel source for cancer cells.[21,22]

I had never paid attention to blood glucose levels except when getting my annual physical and a complete metabolic panel of bloodwork. All those tests had indicated that my blood glucose levels were fine, but only reflected one snapshot in time on one day each year. It is important to track these levels several times throughout the day to see your daily patterns and correlate meals with glucose levels. I find that checking levels before eating the first meal (but not too early), two to three hours after each meal, and before going to bed, works well. For those with insulin resistance, diabetes, or on antidiabetic medications, checking too early in the morning may present abnormally elevated glucose levels due to the "dawn phenomenon."[23] Normal fasting blood glucose levels range from 70–100 mg/dL (milligrams per deciliter) or 3.9–5.6 mmol/L (millimoles per liter).[24] One way a type 2 diabetes diagnosis is confirmed is when fasting glucose reaches 126 mg/dL (7mmol/L) or higher on two separate tests. Ideally, blood glucose levels should be low and stable throughout the day instead of having spikes.

So, I was eating excessive carbohydrates and thinking that the bulge under my belly button was fat. I don't remember when I first noticed the pelvic pooch, but I think it had been there for a few years but perhaps not so large. One day, however, while doing morning yoga postures lying on my stomach, I felt an unusual firmness. This is when I began to grow concerned about the pooch. At first, I thought that a build-up of gas was creating pressure in my intestines. I also questioned whether it could be a tumor, so I water-fasted for a few days, and the firmness went away completely. The pooch became soft again and my pelvic area was noticeably flatter. After that, I didn't think it was a tumor and deduced that it must be gas, so I paid closer attention to my diet and food combining. This all occurred about four months prior to the lumbar MRI.

When I went back for the pelvic MRI a week after the first one, I was hopeful for a confirmation of a benign tumor, but results indicated that it likely was ovarian cancer.

> A large approximately 17.8 x 15.5 x 1.1 cm mixed solid cystic midline pelvic mass extending into the abdominal cavity likely arises from the left ovary and is highly suspicious for an ovarian neoplasm such as serous cystadenocarcinoma versus endometrioid adeno carcinoma (MRI O-RADS category 4 lesion). Recommend OB gyn consult, correlation with CA 125 levels and further evaluation as clinically indicated. Multiple uterine leiomyomas largest measuring up to 4.8 cm.

When I read the full results online (only a snippet is presented here), I experienced a heightened detached calmness that was clearly uncharacteristic for the situation. It was as if some part of my wisdom took over and had been in the background preparing my mind since the first MRI results. Instead of freaking out that I had a large, cancerous tumor on my ovary, I felt as though the Observer within took over. In that moment, I disidentified with the body and identified more with the spirit, something I had experienced for over a decade due to my spiritual practice. I was grateful for my spiritual practice because I knew that without it, I would have been a complete mess after reading this result. This calmness helped me to go on with my workday and start planning next steps. I tried to get an appointment with a gynecologist, but appointments were three months out, and I knew that acting swiftly was paramount. Synchronously, while I was going to get the pelvic MRI, I had run into my father's oncologic urologist, whose wife was also a gynecologist at the hospital. I told him what was happening and that I would like to contact his wife to ask a few questions. He gave me her private number. We talked the next day, and she introduced me to my oncologic gynecologist. Things proceeded quickly from there, and I got an appointment within a few days.

When you hear your oncologist say these three words, "You have cancer," it feels like an omen of death. A heaviness fills your mind and body, and the world as you knew it disappears. Your entire life revolves around cancer from that point forward. The mind, grappling with the unknown, suddenly sinks into a wormhole of doubt and fear. What if I don't recover? How much time do I have left? What will happen to my loved ones if I die? Will I be able to handle what comes next? What will I suffer? How do I tell everyone? What am I going to do about work? Cancer kills with the help of its close allies: fear, doubt, isolation, helplessness, and passivity—everything opposite of wholeness and integration. After my oncologist went over the test results, her recommendations for surgery, and the cancer staging and recovery process, I returned to work that day as usual. Although many feelings arose, I simultaneously was not that affected by them due to years of training in dispassion from my spiritual practice. My mind started focusing instead on the next steps to prepare for surgery, which was only a week away.

To prepare for surgery, my oncologist scheduled a CT scan to examine the chest, abdomen, and pelvis for metastases. A CT scan is a series of X-ray images taken from different angles to create image slices of bones, blood vessels, and tissues.[25] Before the scan, I was given oral iohexol (Omnipaque), a clear liquid iodine-based dye that adds contrast to body parts in the abdomen for clearer imaging. An intravenous (IV) line was also inserted in my arm so that another round of iohexol could be injected after some initial scans. The iodine dye feels warm when it enters your bloodstream and travels to the abdomen, making you feel like you have to urinate. Unlike an MRI test that takes an hour and is a noisy, clanging, jackhammer

Radiation Limits

There is no clear harmful limit for radiation doses from medical scans of less than 100 millisieverts (mSv) in humans, but there is evidence of harmful effects at levels higher than 100 mSv from studies comparing Hiroshima and Nagasaki atomic bomb survivors to the unexposed population.[26] Though difficult to compare a singular intense level of whole body exposure (not to mention the profound psycho-emotional impact of atomic bomb survivors) to incremental radiation exposure focused on specific organs in medical scans, Japanese survivor levels may be used as a reference point. According to the National Cancer Society, radiation exposure levels for chest x-ray, abdominal CT, and full-body PET (positron emission tomography) scans are 0.1, 10, and 25 mSv respectively.[27] At this rate, cancer patients who have several PET scans can rack up well over a 100 mSv in a year or two. In Canada, annual five-year radiation dose limits for nuclear energy workers are 50 and 100 mSv, respectively.[28]

We are exposed to radiation in numerous ways in daily life including medical imaging, cosmic radiation, elevation from sea level, where we live, radon in the air, our food and water, dental crowns, watching TV, computer screen use, playing video games, smoke detectors, etc. For those who are concerned about radiation exposure, online radiation calculators provide estimates in millirem (mrem) that can be converted into mSv.[29]

sounding experience, the CT scan was quiet and only took about 20 minutes. However, I still preferred the MRI over the CT because I suffered intense tinnitus for a few weeks after the scan. I had suffered from tinnitus for decades and could tune it out, but the CT made it abnormally loud. I had attributed the increase to the iodine injection rather than the radiation exposure of the CT scan, but a second scan nine months later didn't cause any increase in tinnitus. Who knows?

Within a few months, I had had one x-ray, one CT scan, and two MRIs. I have never liked being exposed to vibrations from machines or electromagnetic fields (EMFs) from electronic devices, but the MRI did not affect me as negatively as the CT scan, and MRIs do not involve the use of radiation. An MRI machine typically uses a magnet which is 1.5 T (Tesla) that creates a magnetic field that is about 21,000 times greater than the earth's magnetic field.[30] Metal objects, even small ones like paper clips, can become projectiles at approximately 40 mph in these fields, so individuals with pacemakers, metal pins, bars, or clips should get other imaging tests. There are also other risks with MRIs like radio-frequency field skin burns from currents in wires that are close by and cryogenic gas escape during an accidental shutdown of the magnetic field leading to asphyxia, but odds of these occurrences are extremely low. For those who are concerned about radiation exposure, an alternative radiation-free scan is the Prenuvo MRI scanning technology developed by Dr. Rajpaul Attariwala.[31] Apparently, these scans have ten times the resolution, further reduce the number of false positives in cancer screening, take less time, are quiet, and are less claustrophobic than conventional scans. Prenuvo scans can be costly as they are typically not paid for by insurance companies, but in my mind, well worth it if you have already had your radiation allotment for the year as a cancer patient or otherwise.

After the CT scan, results indicated that there was no metastasis in the chest or abdominal organs. I was relieved at this news because it confirmed the MRI results that the tumor was well-confined. Hopeful and positive, I headed toward surgery with the goal of removing the tumor. My oncologist had recommended a total hysterectomy with salpingo-oopherectomy (surgical removal of fallopian tubes and ovaries) because in addition to the tumor on my left ovary, I also had a few benign tumors in my uterus. I was postmenopausal, so having children was not an issue. I learned when blood test and medical imaging results indicate cancer, surgery is typically the first step in diagnosing ovarian cancer. During surgery, samples of the tissue are sent to a pathologist who determines whether they are benign, precancerous, or cancerous. If malignant, samples of nearby organs and lymph nodes will be examined to determine the stage of cancer.

Surgery was only a few days away, so I started prepping my home. I gathered medical supplies, bought baby wipes for sponge baths, organized water delivery, moved a bed into the living room on the first floor, and cleaned the entire house. I did not want my mother—my primary caregiver—to climb the stairs and risk falling, and I knew I wouldn't be able to do any domestic chores during recovery. I wanted to create a peaceful, clean, and beautiful environment to not only minimize germs but to soothe my mind during this process. My oncologist told me that it would take eight weeks to heal from the surgery, so I took FMLA (Family Medical Leave Act) from work which allowed me to keep my job and use sick and vacation days for the time off. Everyone at work was supportive and compassionate. Not worrying about work during this time deeply aided my healing.

Surgery and Diagnosis

My surgery was scheduled for 5:00 AM and I went in feeling grateful and positive. Once you discover you have a large tumor inside your body, you just want to get it out! After changing into a warming gown for surgery and plugging the hot air hose in, I put on my compression socks and had IVs inserted. Several nurses and doctors, like the anesthesiologist, came by to check on me, ask questions, and obtain informed consent. I was thankful for these pre-surgery protocols and realized how necessary they are for the medical team and patient. Surgery is a complex, coordinated process involving many health professionals, so checking on things several times and using good communication is paramount. When I was wheeled into the surgery room, I was surprised by the large team of about ten who were in place and ready to start. The anesthesiologist asked me a few questions, and then I went unconscious—or so I thought. Administration of general anesthesia does not necessarily mean you lose all consciousness. Depending on the type of anesthesia and dose, an individual may experience unconsciousness (absence of subjective experience), disconnected consciousness (dreams), or connected consciousness (awareness of environment).[32] During surgery, I drifted between each of these states. How do I know? I had memories of the procedure after it was over. When I came out of surgery and my awareness reconnected to waking consciousness (like the experience of waking up), a flood of dream-like memories that presented like slide images rapidly came into my mind—similar to the speed of fanning pages in a book with your thumb. I saw the people in the room, my body on the table, and the insertion of the catheter. (I'll have more to say on the mind and consciousness in other sections of this book.)

Surgical procedural notes indicated that during surgery, my feet were placed in Allen stirrups so that my legs were bent to about 90 degrees. Antibiotics were administered through the IV. Pubic hair was shaved and then the body was draped. In addition to the hysterectomy, I was also getting a biopsy to check for lichen sclerosis in the outer genital area because I had been experiencing constant itching even after trying a variety of ointments, raw aloe vera, and medicated oils. The itching may have come from hormonal shifts after menopause. A 3 mm biopsy was taken for pathological examination and then the skin area was sutured with an absorbable stitch. The lichen sclerosis results came back negative. Incidentally, a salve from MJ Herbals that I found online reduced the itching by about 80 percent. I suspect it may have been the addition of Oregon grape root—or perhaps the combined efficacy of ingredients—as I had already tried several of the other ingredients without success.

After the first biopsy was taken, my oncologist used electrocautery to make an approximately 18-centimeter incision from the sternum to the pubis that carried down to the fascia (connective tissue). The fascia was cut to enter the peritoneal cavity that houses digestive, urinary, and reproductive organs. A self-retaining retractor was inserted to hold the space open, and pelvic washings were obtained to assess the presence of any metastasis. My surgeon then worked on clamping off blood loss from ligaments.

A big portion of the tumor had attached onto part of the colon, obstructing the view of that area. My surgeon had to free that up. As surgery continued, the tumor ruptured, creating a surgical spill. Old blood was drained. The remaining parts of the tumor were removed with sharp (cutting with scissors or scalpel) and blunt (separating tissue rather than cutting) dissection and then handed off for frozen section analysis (rapid microscopic examination of a specimen). Because I was also having the uterus and cervix removed, a vaginal cuff closure was made at the top of the vagina where the cervix had been. Then, the abdomen and pelvis were irrigated, and tissues were sealed to prevent blood loss. The next steps were excising the lymph nodes for examination and removing the omentum. Then, the abdomen and pelvis were washed again, the fascia was closed, the skin was reconnected with staples, and the anesthesia was reversed. The surgery had taken 2–3 hours.

A word of caution: I present my surgery process to describe what happened to me, but hysterectomies (there are other less invasive procedures than abdominal surgeries) and ovarian cancer tumor excision are not the same for everyone. Each individual's physical presentation is different. Generally, though, there are good resources online to understand surgical processes for both.[33,34] In a total hysterectomy, the uterus, one or more ovaries, and fallopian tubes are removed. In my case, I had a total *radical* hysterectomy where the uterus, cervix, both ovaries, fallopian tubes, and omentum (flat tissue layer surrounding abdominal cavity organs) were removed.[35] I also had 17 lymph nodes excised for cancer staging. During surgery, samples of the tissue were sent to the pathologist for cancer staging (identifying the stage of cancer). For ovarian cancer, there are two classification systems: the FIGO (International Federation of Gynecology and Obstetrics) that uses the I-IVB system, and the AJCC (American Joint Committee on Cancer) that uses the TNM (T=tumor size, N=spread to nearby lymph nodes, M=metastasis) coding system.[36] My pathology report later indicated "endometrioid adenocarcinoma IC1 N0," which meant that cancer was present in one or more ovaries or fallopian tubes. It also noted that there was a surgical spill during the tumor extraction which could have allowed cancer cells to enter the abdomen and pelvis.

Recovery in the Hospital

After surgery, I was wheeled into the recovery room. I was drifting in and out of waking consciousness and heard the recovery nurse say that my blood pressure was low. I tend to be hypotensive (low blood pressure) and managed to inform the nurse. I heard him say that I might need a blood transfusion because my blood pressure was *so* low. I really hoped this wouldn't be the case because I would then need to go to the ICU. The nurse kept me in the recovery room for five hours until my blood pressure got a little higher. It still wasn't in a "normal" range, but for me, normal was on the low side. I was finally released to the hospital room. I was mostly unconscious during this time.

The Body

I became fully conscious when the hospital staff transferred me from the surgery bed to the hospital room bed. My mother, who had been waiting for me in the room, was the first person I saw. (During the COVID-19 pandemic, only one visitor per day could be in the room.) After being lifted onto the bed, I felt a wave of emotion come over me and began to cry. I felt a strong sense of compassion for my body and the trauma it had just been through. It was especially difficult for my mother to see me sobbing, and she told me not to cry—her way of soothing me. I told her through my tears, "I can't help it, momma." Typically a calm person, I was surprised by the sudden and strong urge to cry. I realized that these emotions were coming from somewhere deep within and had been suppressed for a long time and needed to be expressed. (The mental and spiritual origins of these emotions will be explained later.) After a few more tears, I was able to talk with my mother. I was not feeling much pain because the general anesthesia, spinal anesthesia, and pain medication were still in effect. I was also given oxycodone and acetaminophen for pain relief and ibuprofen to reduce the inflammation.

The next three days were a blur of compassionate nurses, health technicians, residents, therapists, social workers, and doctors. Blood draws and vital sign checks were routine. My doctor told me I should try to get up from the bed and walk a little bit to help with recovery. This presented a mental challenge because my natural instinct was to not move at all. The first day after surgery, I had my first experience of lying supine for over 24 hours. I felt like any jostling would be damaging. When my body slid down too far on the bed, I asked the nurses to help pull me up. I could not sit up by myself, but the mechanical hospital bed did that for me with a push of a button. I had a "FALL RISK" bracelet on my arm indicating that I needed help to be ambulatory, but the catheter was still in place, so I didn't need to get up to urinate. I wasn't really eating much so there weren't any bowel movements. When food was delivered to my room the first day, I could not imagine eating. I had no appetite, but I was surprised by the standard fare of the meals; nutritional quality had a long way to go in conventional care after surgery. Anticipating this, I had asked my mother to bring me organic bananas blended with water or freshly squeezed carrot juice. Still, I had no appetite even though I wasn't nauseous—a typical outcome of anesthesia. At the end of the second day, I started wanting to go home to a more peaceful environment where I could focus on healing. My oncologist told me that I would be able to go home when I could do three things: get out of bed by myself, walk around a little, and pass gas.

Motivated by the conditions for discharge, I got out of bed, sat in the chair, and walked around the room with my IV pole in tow. The electronic bed propped me forward to a sitting position, but getting my torso in place and fully upright, hanging my legs over the side of the bed, and pushing off the bed to a standing position were extremely challenging. Moving slowly, I had to use my arms to support every movement. Each time it took me several minutes and was always a major accomplishment! I would instinctively hold my stomach with one hand for support; using abdominal muscles after they've been cut is painful. My mother, who had been through abdominal surgery for stomach cancer, warned me to be careful not to get a cold, as sneezing or coughing would make me miserable. The nurse had suggested that I also walk outside my room along the corridor. Walking parallel with my mother, I made one revolution—another victory! When you are this weak, the days seem filled with such "minor" achievements: swallowing medications, getting out of bed, sitting in a chair, walking, eating, urinating, passing gas, and making a bowel movement. You are fully in the body focusing on movement, coordination, tension, release, and function. I was happy to see the parade of health professionals who came and went and enjoyed chatting with them. Although my body was suffering, I still felt positive and even cheerful at times. A friend also came to visit which was wonderful for my mood. I cannot say enough about the healing power of social support.

Leading up to the surgery, one of my dearest friends

had helped me to prepare. A biostatistician by profession, she was experienced with medical studies and served as an informative resource. I also knew I could trust and rely on her. I have never been good at asking for help—typically relying on myself instead—so it was a relief to have such a caring and dependable ally. I had asked her to coordinate post-surgery communication to my relatives, friends, and colleagues because I didn't think I would have the energy to respond to everyone. This was a good call, because after surgery, I wanted to be shielded even from the most well-intentioned. I needed to be in a protective cocoon to conserve all my energy to heal. The last thing I needed was to be too stimulated or stressed. I highly recommend having an advocate or coordinator for your post-surgery care and communication. If it's possible to split these duties up between a few individuals, even better. Living with cancer is sometimes more stressful for caregivers, especially if they feel as if they don't have a choice in the matter.[37] Also, caregivers can experience information overload regardless of their health literacy.[38] If possible, select individuals who can manage the tasks you need help with. If they aren't available, choose those who truly desire to help you. They will always have your best interests in mind regardless of how much they know or don't know about cancer.

One of the issues you have to face after receiving a cancer diagnosis is informing others. Some people may want to keep it to themselves until they are ready to make it public. Some may only tell a select few, and others will openly invite people into their process. Once you go public, you take on the mantle of "cancer identity." From that point forward, you are known as a cancer *fighter, survivor, victim,* etc. Your old identity sloughs away and henceforth becomes synonymous with cancer, even though who you really are extends far beyond these labels. Making your diagnosis public feels like opening the sluice gates to a flood of sympathy while trying to manage the levels of your own watery emotions. Some people look at you as if you are a dead person walking and others with grave concern. Most want to know how they can help and do not consider it a burden to do so. Helping others opens the heart which is its own reward. People can say prayers for you, cover your work responsibilities, help research medical questions, clean the house, pick up your medications, order supplements, drive you to appointments, get groceries, visit to uplift your mood, deliver meals, and donate money.

After surgery, I noticed that the top of my right thigh was numb. I asked about it and was told that it was probably from the anesthesia and should wear off. When it persisted, I started to worry. I had lost all sensation but fortunately not function (no paralysis). After being released from the hospital, I had started to have a strong itching sensation (neuropathic itch) on my right thigh along with numbness.[39]

I learned that femoral nerve damage was one possible complication from abdominal, pelvic, and lower limb surgery from either direct trauma or retraction (stretching of the nerve).[40] My oncologist confirmed that the right general femoral nerve could have been damaged or even cut during surgery as it was the size of a strand of hair. I was alarmed to hear this because I wondered if the numbness would be permanent. I was told that it should improve over time but could take from six months to a year. The aftermath of these types of injuries are usually temporary, although there are cases of long-term dysfunction.[41] Thankfully, I noticed that as the months passed by, sensation gradually returned.

While I was in the hospital, I did not want to look at the incision. After stitching up and stapling the skin together, the surgical team glued a long strip of medical tape to cover the sutures and then placed a long, wide absorbent pad on top of the tape. I was grateful for the pad because it provided a little cushion under the thin hospital gown. A part of me didn't want to look underneath the pad because I was afraid of what I would see. Although it's important to check incision sites for signs of swelling and infection, I needed another day to gather up my courage. My body is highly sensitive, and I do not like the sight of blood. Even cutting meat is hard. For me, the psychological turmoil was not about "disfigurement," even though this is a valid and common concern.[42] I just didn't want a reminder of the trauma itself. It was difficult to admit what had happened to my body. Under anesthesia, I didn't experience any pain, so when I lay still, it was as if nothing horrible had happened to me. By the second day, I peeked under the pad and saw a long row of staples underneath the tape. It was shocking! The incision was so long, I looked like a stitched-up Frankenstein! To be fair to the surgical team, the incision was straight except where it curved around the belly button and healed nicely, but at the time, I only saw a grotesque reminder of the operation. Although I knew I wasn't *only* the body, the surgery dislodged traumatic memories of painful surgeries from long ago that I will explore later in the book.

Recovery at Home

After three days in the hospital, I was discharged. My thoughtful friend had borrowed her father's car to take me home because it was a smoother ride, but I still felt my insides jostling with every little bump in the road. After picking up pain and blood-thinning medication, I finally arrived home! It was wonderful to be back in my own space where I could focus on healing. My mother had prepared the house and tended to the beautiful flowers that friends had sent. I really appreciated those flowers because they brought the healing power of nature's beauty into the environment.

Still groggy from all the medications I'd been taking, I

needed help sorting out the schedule of multiple medications going forward, so my dear friend hand wrote a timetable for the next three days. My mother was like an angel hovering around me. She cooked all my meals, did light cleaning, went grocery shopping, and kept me company when I was awake. Not a big talker, she intentionally just sat beside my bed holding my hand in silence. I felt so loved and supported by her. Our roles had reversed, because it was usually me who helped her and went to her house to check on her. Pre-surgery, I had not spent the quality time I wanted with my mother due to my busy, hectic life and daily routines. She had also become increasingly introverted and quiet after the death of my brother and father as well as her recent aneurysm. Her loving attention, along with my weakened condition, brought out my inner child. We would sit in silence holding hands and gaze into each other's eyes. It was true intimacy and deeply healing.

During the first two weeks of recovery, I slept most of the time. I was taking acetaminophen, ibuprofen, and oxycodone for post-surgical pain on a staggered basis, and the latter two made me drowsy. The only time I got up was to use the bathroom or walk a bit in the room. I used my father's old walker; the same one my mother had used. When I realized how the walker had been passed down through my family, I felt sad. I weighed about 118 lbs (53.5 kgs) after surgery. My highest weight had been approximately 150

_# The Body

lbs (68 kgs) in the year proceeding, so over that period, I had lost a lot of weight—another sign that something was wrong. Surprisingly, removing the tumor did not lower my weight that much; I only lost about 3–5 lbs. I had heard stories of people having 20–50 lb tumors, so I thought my tumor would weigh more, but even a mid-sized cantaloupe weighs only 3 lbs.

Around 2:00 each morning, I would wake up and just lie in bed in the darkness. Sounds depressing, but it was very peaceful, like floating on your back in water. My mother would come by with an early breakfast around 6:30. The first few days, all I could eat was warm rice porridge, eggs, and freshly squeezed carrot juice. Moist and soft foods was what I naturally wanted. I was averse to anything hot due to my delicate insides. My mother encouraged me to eat more, but I still did not have much of an appetite. It felt like my body was conserving its energy for healing and did not want to expend anything for digestion, especially with medications circulating in my body. A geriatrician friend urged me to eat more protein. She said it was the single best thing I could do to heal and stop muscle loss. The recommended dietary allowance (RDA) for adults was .80 grams per kilogram of body weight,[43] but more recent research has indicated that higher levels of protein (1.2 to 1.6 grams per kilogram of body weight) is more ideal for optimizing health.[44] Increased protein consumption has also

37

been associated with fewer post-operative complications and rehospitalizations.[45] Using the higher requirement, I needed between 64 to 85 grams of protein daily. My physician friend had recommended I eat at least 70 grams of protein each day starting with four egg whites. So, I told my mother, and she immediately started Operation Protein. Two egg whites at breakfast, two at lunch, fish protein, and a protein shake became the norm. It was challenging to eat so much protein without much of an appetite and also because carbohydrates were typically the major portion of my meals. I was to learn later that a high-protein diet was not good for cancer, but after surgery, the body needs high protein levels to heal, so recovery trumped everything initially.

In my presurgery consultation with my oncologist, I learned that some possible complications included damage to nearby organs. Fortunately, once the catheter was removed, I was able to urinate without any problems, especially after watching my father's struggles. The tumor had adhered to my colon, so I was most concerned about injury to this area. I had not made had a bowel movement during my hospital stay even though I had started taking stool softeners. After surgery, I couldn't bear down due to internal sutures and pain, so I was relieved when my first bowel movement occurred easily with the help of a stool softener after being at home for two days. The bowel is just one part of the digestive system from mouth to anus, but a key organ in wellness.[46] Feeling good after a bowel movement is not just in the mind but also in the body. This psychophysiological effect has been coined "poo-phoria" by Dr. Anish Steth and Josh Richman.[47] This euphoric feeling comes from stimulating the vagus nerve, the longest cranial nerve that starts in the brain and ends in the colon. This large nerve helps regulate breathing, heart rate, and mood, and its stimulation offers therapeutic promise for irritable bowel syndrome (IBS).[48]

My surgeon had prescribed 28 days of blood-thinning medication to prevent post-surgery blood clotting. Blood clots can get stuck in veins and prevent blood from reaching organs, which can cause heart attacks, strokes, and permanent damage to organs.[49] After the fourth day on the medication, I developed an itchy red rash on my inner calves, the outer pelvic area by the hip bones, and close by the incision site. It was as if my body tissues were internally enflamed, and any scratching on the skin resulted in raised red bumps. I had been taking the blood thinner apixaban (Eliquis) but suffered a bad reaction to it. When I informed the oncology nurses, they had me switch to enoxaparin (Lovenox), which had to be injected subcutaneously. It took me a few minutes to gather my courage before self-injecting the medicine. The best place was in the abdomen where there was more fat, but with the incision site being so sensitive, I had to be careful not to pinch skin close to the site. If I positioned the needle at a 45-degree angle, the insertion wasn't painful; however, if the angle was wider than that, it was painful. The medication also stung a little going in. No matter how many times I did it, I still felt a little queasy.

After a few days of using the enoxaparin, I still had the rash and wondered if I could use something else. My oncologist told me that the only other thing I could use would be baby aspirin (81 mg), which is about one-fourth the dose of an adult aspirin pill (325 mg). Around day 20 of taking the blood thinners, I decided to switch to baby aspirin because the rash was not improving. I intentionally walked more and started using leg pump massagers to help with blood flow. I also knew that turmeric was a natural blood thinner, but I didn't know the dosage I would need so I continued with the aspirin even though my stomach had never felt good after taking it. Long-term use of aspirin can increase the risk of bleeding, but I was only going to be using it for a week. Blood clot formation, especially after surgery when you aren't moving much, is a serious matter and patients should follow their doctor's advice. I wanted to take the prescribed medications, but I had such a bad reaction that I couldn't do it. If you find yourself in this situation, always ask for alternatives, and weigh the pros and cons given your health status.

Chemotherapy or Not?

One week after surgery, I had my follow-up appointment with the advanced practice nurse (APRN) to remove the staples. The procedure only took a few minutes and didn't hurt. It was the first time I could see the incision in the raw, and it was still hard to look at. The nurse glued on a row of about 20 short medical strips that would fall off in a few weeks on their own. Psychologically, it felt good to have a protective covering over the incision. My next appointment was the first follow-up with my oncologist after surgery. During my hospital stay, she came to check on me during rounds daily. I asked her if she thought I would need chemotherapy, and she said that while we would need to wait for the full pathology report, probably yes. I felt disappointed but thought I would go ahead with chemotherapy if necessary.

While at home recovering, I had an intuition that I wouldn't need chemotherapy, and the pathology report turned out to be encouraging. The cancer was found at an early stage, so I was hopeful that surgery would be enough. At the follow-up with my oncologist, though, I met with a cancer care social worker who gave me a bag of "ovarian cancer goodies" like a knit cap, shawl, pins, notebooks, etc. She started talking about the possibility of getting wigs, and I wondered why because I wouldn't be needing chemotherapy, right? My oncologist came in and broke the news that because of spillage during the tumor debulking, cancer cells could have spread outside the tumor sac. She recommended six rounds of chemotherapy as an adjuvant after surgery as per the standard protocol. I was crushed to hear this because I was so hopeful that I didn't need it. I asked her for the pros and cons of moving forward with and without the chemo. She said there was a good chance of curing the cancer with chemotherapy and a 35 percent chance of it returning in five years without chemotherapy. Treatment risks included a compromised immune system (white and red blood cell loss), gastrointestinal damage, nerve damage (potentially long-term), hair loss, loss of taste, metallic taste in mouth, mouth sores, loss of appetite, nausea, vomiting, light sensitivity, weight loss, tinnitus, bruising, peeling of the skin, and fatigue. I asked her if there was any alternative besides chemo, and she said no. I continued to ask more questions and had the feeling that she wasn't used to talking so long with patients in these post-surgery follow-ups. She seemed ready to leave for the next patient, and it was clear she thought chemotherapy was the only way moving forward. She did say that if I didn't do well after the first infusion, one possibility might be reducing the rounds from six to four.

I felt uneasy and a little rushed but agreed to the first infusion date in two weeks. One thing that shocked me was learning that standard procedure is to start chemotherapy one month after surgery to prevent potential metastasis. I was barely starting to heal, and I couldn't imagine trying to deal simultaneously with healing after major organ removal as well as chemotherapy. The poor body!

I went home and tried to digest all the information. One of the most challenging aspects of a cancer diagnosis is that you feel rushed to act due to the speed at which cancer grows. Healthcare professionals, who must follow the current structure and protocols of the medical system, also feel this pressure, and they often assume that standard treatment is obvious to their patients. They don't understand—or perhaps have become desensitized to—the fact that patients need time to process the deluge of information both mentally and emotionally before making life-altering decisions. I was grateful for the few weeks I had before the first infusion because thanks to intuition, reflection, and research, my path forward became clearer. Chemotherapy was not an option that both my mind and heart would agree on. I mean whenever I unknowingly ate a little MSG in my food, I couldn't handle it, so how would I ever be able to manage a poisonous carcinogen like chemotherapy? I wasn't concerned about chemotherapy's effectiveness; I knew it could be effective. It was the long-term effects that worried me, because even if you lived longer, what would be the quality of your life? Without your health, you really cannot live life. (I learned later that chemotherapy can also create therapy-related, secondary cancers.[50-52])

The chemotherapy medications that my oncologist prescribed were the platinum-based agent carboplatin (Paraplatin) and the plant-derived taxane paclitaxel (Taxol, Onxal). These drugs damage RNA or DNA that prevent cancer cells from self-replication or transcription (copying DNA strands into new messenger RNA).[53] Unable to divide, cancer cells die through a process called *apoptosis* (cellular suicide).[54] Having a history of sensitivity to medications, I had never been keen on taking them and preferred herbal products that did not produce side effects. For those who may not know and are inclined toward more natural products, many chemotherapeutic agents are actually derived from plants or tree bark.[55,56] Additionally, even herbal supplements can have unwanted side effects, especially when taken with prescription medications, and should be used with caution.[57] Information on herbs, vitamins, and over-the counter (OTC) supplements is available online.[58-61] When it came to chemotherapy, though, I was more concerned with its toxic effects rather than whether or not it was natural.

For ovarian cancer, cisplatin or carboplatin, both alkylating agents, are usually prescribed. These drugs work by damaging the DNA and, in the process, they damage cells in the bone marrow where new blood cells are created.

Chemotherapy Drugs Target Specific Phases of the Cell Cycle

After being formed, a single cell undergoes a maturation process just as a baby becomes an adult. This process is called "the cell cycle" and involves several phases. Chemotherapy drugs work by targeting specific phases in the cycle to break down cellular development and destroy cancer cells.[62] Some of these drugs work throughout all phases of the cell cycle (non-specific) and others are effective during a specific phase (cell-cycle specific).

Chemotherapy agents are classically defined by their chemical structure and mechanism of action and classified into six main categories:

1. alkylating agents that stop cell division;
2. antibiotics that disrupt protein creation necessary for cell survival;
3. antimetabolites that disrupt cell metabolism and protein synthesis;
4. topoisomerases inibitors that disrupt enzymes from separating DNA strands for replication;
5. mitosis inhibitors that keep cells from dividing by arresting enzymes from making proteins;
6. and others that do not fit easily into the other five categories.[63,64]

Chemotherapy not only destroys cancerous cells but also healthy ones, so when blood cells are destroyed, cancerous cells (leukemia) can develop.[65,66] The other drug that is typically prescribed for ovarian cancer is a taxane such as paclitaxel. This chemotherapeutic drug can cause nerve damage.[67,68]

When I first found out I had ovarian cancer, I was told about survival rate data which come from the National Cancer Institute's SEER (Surveillance, Epidemiology, and End Results) population database.[69] These statistics compare whether those with the same cancer and stage are still living five years later compared to the general population's mortality rates. Grouped into different stages than AJCC or FIGO, SEER database records are categorized into three stages for ovarian cancer based upon spread from origin: localized (no metastases outside ovaries), regional (metastases to nearby tissues or ovaries), and distant (metastases to distant parts of body).[70] For ovarian cancer, the 5-year survival rate for epithelial ovarian cancer (originating on the surface layer of the ovary) is 93% localized, 75% regional, and 31% distant. These statistics reflect the stage of cancer at initial diagnosis and not whether the cancer has grown, spread, or reoccurred after treatment. Survival rates neither indicate how many people survived after chemotherapy (versus without it) nor reveal the quality of their lives.

I need to be clear here because I am not saying that patients should never choose chemotherapy. It truly depends on each person's will, health status, diagnosis, lifestyle, resources, and support. Moreover, it's an individual decision. In my case, I was seriously concerned about side effects, quality of life, and therapy-related recurrence after chemotherapy, which is why I presented this information — to show my thought process. I needed time to research ovarian cancer and its possible treatments. Although I am not a licensed health professional, I know how to conduct research; however, you don't need to be a trained researcher to become better informed. You can go to Google Scholar, type in any cancer, and read just the abstracts (summaries) if it's too challenging to read the entire study. Don't be intimidated by the statistics or medical jargon. You can always look up medical terms one at a time. Look for studies that have been peer-reviewed, which means that the study has been scrutinized by others knowledgeable in that topic. Search for the journal in which the research article was published to see if it uses the peer-review process. If this is too much after being diagnosed with cancer, ask friends to help. Little by little, you will understand more than you did the day before and become more empowered. Many researchers also have videos on YouTube with more comprehensible presentations, and there are multiple online forums and in-person support groups for every type of cancer. There are many resources to better understand cancer, treatment, effects, and other related issues. Though with everything on the internet, recognize the difference between opinions and facts. Get your information from credible sources as much as possible.

Prior to the first chemotherapy infusion, the drugs dexamethasone (Decadron), ondansetron (Zofran-ODT), and prochlorperazine (Compazine) were prescribed. Dexamethasone is a steroid that reduces inflammation and is taken the day before each chemotherapy infusion; ondansetron and prochlorperazine prevent nausea and vomiting afterwards. A friend had picked up these medications for me, but I was still conflicted about doing chemo and the first infusion was just two weeks away. I had just stopped using pain medication from the surgery and felt like I was making some progress in recovery, so having chemo looming over me was daunting. One early morning, I was lying in bed meditating when I had a strong feeling that I should not do chemotherapy. I needed to trust my earlier intuition that I didn't need chemotherapy despite what my oncologist recommended. Despite the rationale behind chemotherapy, my conflicted feelings were another sign that it wasn't right for me. If the mind and heart are not in agreement, the path forward will be more challenging. I could not accept the contradiction between the Hippocratic ideal of "do no harm" and doing great harm to the body, even if that ideal has been criticized as unrealistic for the modern physician.[71]

If I didn't do chemo, though, what *should* I do? I did not want to do nothing, because if there is even one cancer cell left in the body, it can proliferate. What really helped me during this doubtful period was silence, calm, thinking, reflecting, dreaming, prayer, and meditating. I cannot overpraise listening to your inner self. Mentally, I understood the pros and cons of chemotherapy; emotionally, I was conflicted about it; spiritually, I felt the support of a much greater power than my personal self. Each aspect of myself was telling me something about the way forward if I could be receptive enough to hear these subtle messages. In retrospect, the recovery period created prime conditions of stillness, rest, and quiet that I needed in order to hear my inner self, especially in the early morning hours.

Having experience with fasting, I was familiar with Dr. Jason Fung's work and decided to order his book, *The Cancer Code*. I wanted to understand what cancer was, because despite my entire family having had it, I still knew little about it. The simple act of ordering this book, precipitated by inward subtle focusing and listening, was the first step in a long, empowering journey. Reading Dr. Fung's book led to researching the effectiveness of fasting for cancer. I had fasted several times previously to detoxify my body or help it heal, so I had experienced its benefits. I had even worked up to prolonged fasts unsupervised, but knew I needed supervision and support if I were to use fasting for cancer. This led me to discover Dr. Valter Longo's research on both intermittent fasting to prevent diseases and the "fasting-mimicking diet" as an effective adjunct to chemotherapy.[72-74] I contacted Dr. Longo, who was sincere and supportive. He quickly connected me to his Create Cures Foundation Clinic that works with people interested in fasting. Unfortunately, I found out that telehealth appointments would be difficult to do for someone living in Arkansas due to licensing rules. I would have to drive to Oklahoma just to have an online appointment, so I didn't pursue this further. Another factor that dissuaded me from using the fasting-mimicking diet was my need at that time for additional calories and protein to recover from surgery. The clinic's low-calorie diet also used prepackaged boxed meals, and I knew I needed a whole food diet.

A Metabolic Approach to Cancer

Undeterred, I resumed my research. My daily routine was a combination of sleeping, resting, eating, researching, and meditating, most of which was done lying down. One day as I was transitioning from meditation to external reorientation, I heard my inner voice say "Boston." A few days later, I saw a video presentation on YouTube by Dr. Thomas Seyfried on cancer as a metabolic disease.[75] After watching the video, I intuitively and rationally understood that Dr. Seyfried was correct about cancer. Everything he said made sense, and I appreciated his research, common sense, frankness, and sincerity. When I found out that he was at Boston College, it was an affirming synchronicity.

In the 1920s, Dr. Otto Warburg, a German physiologist, physician, and Nobel laureate (1931), observed that cancer cells, unlike healthy cells, fermented glucose (an anaerobic process) at abnormally high rates even when sufficient oxygen was present.[76] He called this phenomenon "aerobic glycolysis." Fermentation as a metabolic process was the only way to produce energy billions of years ago, before our atmosphere had the levels of oxygen now needed to sustain life.[77] But cancer cells were employing that same primitive fermentation, converting glucose—a simple sugar found in almost all carbohydrate-containing foods—into lactate even though this process was not an efficient way to produce energy. Fermentation of glucose in the cytoplasm of cells only yielded 2 ATP (energy-carrying molecules) per glucose molecule compared to 32 ATP per glucose molecule when glucose underwent oxidative respiration in the mitochondria of healthy cells.[78] Paradoxically, cancer cells chose this inefficient route. Electron microscopy, not available in Warburg's time, has revealed that almost all cancer cells have damaged mitochondria—the organelle of the cell that generates the majority of the chemical energy needed for biochemical reactions.

In the decades since Warburg's observation, the original understanding of why cancer cells ferment has evolved to include the observation that cancer cells use fermentation byproducts to build new cancer cells. In fact, this now appears to be the main driver behind the switch from oxidation to fermentation.[79] Unfortunately, research was derailed as researchers turned their attention away from the "Warburg effect" with the discovery of DNA's structure and the movement towards understanding the human genome. With that came the current flawed paradigm that genetic mutations were the *cause* rather than the *effect* of dysfunctional mitochondria. Thankfully, a thread of that original research was kept alive and then built upon by Dr. Peter Pederson and later, Dr. Seyfried.[80-81] Dr. Seyfried's research indicated that not only glucose, but glutamine was an additional and compensatory source of fuel for cancer cells. This meant that in addition to sugar, cancer cells could ferment proteins, especially glutamine, for energy despite structural defects in their mitochondria. Mitochondrial fermentation also produced building blocks for new cancer cells.

I knew that sugar (carbohydrates) fed cancer cells and was confident that I could eliminate most of the sugars in my diet, but protein had me concerned. What would I eat instead? The answer turned out to be a *ketogenic* diet that is high in fat. "Therapeutic" levels of the ketogenic diet have been shown to be anti-tumor, anti-angiogenic (inhibiting the vascular structure that cancer cells create to fuel growth), anti-inflammatory, and pro-apoptotic (encouraging cell death) in mice.[82] One patient with glioblastoma, an aggressive cancer in the brain or spinal cord, has been managing his cancer for over six years without chemotherapy or radiation using a therapeutic ketogenic diet with a more rigorous combination of low glucose and high ketone levels than a ketogenic diet for weight loss purposes.[83]

One idea that resonated with me was Dr. Seyfried and his collaborators' press-pulse conceptualization for the metabolic management of cancer.[84] Using paleobiologists Nan Arens and Ian West's theory on the mass decimation of organic populations, Seyfried and his colleagues likened the extinction of cancer cells to that of living populations.[85] A *press* is a long-term stressor on organisms, whereas a *pulse* is a singular disturbance that produces high mortality. For example, a starving population would be under chronic nutritional stress (press), and many people would perish. If a major epidemic occurred (pulse) during that period, it would decimate the population because the organisms had already been weakened by chronic stress. For complete extinction, using the press and the pulse simultaneously was necessary. The ketogenic diet (press) creates metabolic stress on cancer cells' energy metabolism. When used in tandem with glucose and glutamine inhibition (pulse therapies), the results are more effective than using one alone.

I contacted Dr. Seyfried, explained my diagnosis, and said that I did not want to do chemotherapy. He graciously sent me an information resource kit and several publications that he had compiled. He also made it clear that he was not a medical doctor and could not treat patients or give medical advice. He asked that I send him an acknowledgement email stating that I understood, which I did. The information kit included contacts for nutritionists, doctors, and integrative oncologists who were familiar with the metabolic approach to cancer. (Most conventional health professionals are not.) It also highlighted several resources that included videos, books, and blogs from people who had eliminated late stage and even terminal cancers. Dr. Seyfried was a Promethean figure bringing light into the darkness of cancer. Compassionate, innovative researchers like him are invaluable to humanity.

Around that same time, I had discovered Joe Tippen's blog, "Get Busy Living," while researching online.[86] He was diagnosed with small cell lung cancer (SCLC). It eventually spread throughout his entire body, and he was given three months to live. Tippens was an Oklahoma State University fan and came across a post on its sports board that said, "If you have cancer or know someone who does, give me a shout." He contacted the author of the post and learned about a scientist at Merck Animal Health who had discovered that a canine deworming medication had eradicated all sorts of malignant tumors in mice. This scientist had been diagnosed with terminal brain cancer and was also told she had three months to live. Having nothing to lose, she started taking the canine anti-parasitic and, six weeks later, her tumors had disappeared. Tippens also began taking the dog dewormer (Merck's Panacur C) along with curcumin and cannabidiol (CBD) oil and, three months later, his PET scan did not show a single trace of tumors in his body. His story went viral, and people started buying the dog dewormer in droves. His eponymous protocol (Tippens protocol) is available on his blog along with an updated version of it. Those with cancer or their loved ones can request to be added to his Facebook group. I joined the group and was so inspired by all the success stories people were posting for all types of cancer and stages. His group is an excellent resource for sharing information, encouragement, and support. I was further motivated when I searched online for Panacur C and saw even more people posting positive reviews, not about treatment for their dogs but for themselves or their loved ones with cancer!

Dr. Seyfried's information kit had also included Tippen's blog, so it was further confirmation that an anthelmintic (antiparasitic) could work to destroy cancerous cells. Anthelmintics disrupt cancer cell environments broadly by disturbing their vasculature, triggering cell suicide, disrupting the cell cycle (G2/M), and blocking glucose transport.[87] This class of antiparasitics is called benzimidazole anthelmintics and include, but are not limited to, albendazole, mebendezole, fenbendazole, and flubendazole. Typically, antiparasitics are prescribed to remove parasites but they can be repurposed for cancer treatment and hold great promise to this end.[88] Cancer medications are costly to develop as the entire process, from drug development to clinical trials to FDA approval, can cost up to two billion dollars.[89] Existing medications that have already been approved by the FDA could be reused for other purposes and would reduce time and expenses, but it appears that research to discover novel uses for existing drugs (whether during initial drug testing or later) is rarely undertaken and decreases to almost nothing when generic drugs become available.[90]

The canine antiparasitic that Tippens used was fenbendazole, whereas the one prescribed for humans is typically mebendazole. A prescription is not required to buy fenbendazole because it is a canine medication that can be purchased online or in general merchandise or animal supply stores. Mebendazole, however, does require a physician's prescription. Initially, I was concerned about using fenbendazole because, to the best of my knowledge, there had not been any human studies, although there had been mouse studies that showed antitumorigenic effects.[91-92] The most I could find on fenbendazole was Merck's Material Safety Data Sheet on Panacur granules, which pointed toward mebendazole (same chemical class) for potential side effects in humans. I was not as concerned about mebendazole as it had already been approved by the FDA and had a long history of low toxicity and good tolerability in humans.[93] After reading other cancer survivor success stories and doing further research, I figured it was fairly safe to start taking mebendezole. People were not reporting serious side effects from fenbendazole, and mebendazole was well tolerated, so I ordered 10 packets (ten 3-day supplies) of Merck's Panacur C online. Each packet was the daily dose for a 10-lb dog so I wasn't too concerned considering I weighed much more than that. Tippens had warned against an increase in Panacur C knock-offs in the market and to be wary of their ingredients, so I ordered the Merck brand. The Tippens protocol originally was three days of 222 mgs of fenbendazole and four days off. Similar doses of mebendazole were recommended to treat parasites in children, so it seemed that the dose was safe.[94] Tippens had been diagnosed as terminal and took fenbendazole for three months at this dose with astonishing success. He also hadn't changed his diet or anything else during this time. I decided to follow the original protocol (minus the CBD oil) until my next CA-125 test about five weeks away. I had an early-stage cancer and was about to start a therapeutic ketogenic diet, so I was hopeful a press-pulse effect would occur.

Changing to a Ketogenic Diet

Through Dr. Seyfried's information kit and my own research,

I kept circling back to Miriam Kalamian, nutritionist and author of *Keto for Cancer*. Miriam is a passionate advocate for utilizing a ketogenic diet therapeutically for cancer patients. Her young son, Raffi, was diagnosed with a brain tumor in 2004 and went through chemotherapy, surgery, and multiple anticancer drugs. During that time, there was little research on the ketogenic diet for cancer, but she came across a paper written by Dr. Seyfried, who had been working on the effects of a ketogenic diet on glioblastoma in mice.[95] Anti-seizure effects from implementing a ketogenic diet in epileptic children had been studied since the 1920s but not much existed for cancer.[96] She later went on to get a master's degree in nutrition to better help her son. Talk about being empowered! Sadly, Raffi passed away in 2013, but the ketogenic diet prolonged the precious time they had together for another six years and improved his quality of life during that time.

After coming home from the hospital, I initially ate whatever my mother prepared for me such as white rice, fish, broccoli, eggs, and carrot juice. When I realized that I needed to keep my blood glucose low, I reduced my carbohydrate intake but kept protein high to speed recovery. I had been tracking blood glucose levels with a glucometer, but I did not start a therapeutic ketogenic diet until I started working with Miriam. For cancer patients, a therapeutic level of ketosis is higher than for those who use the diet for weight loss. For cancer, the glucose ketone index (GKI) is a good measure for targeting and monitoring therapeutic levels of blood glucose and ketones.[97] There are two measurements to take to determine the GKI: blood glucose and blood ketones. Ideally, for cancer, you want to have lower glucose and higher ketone levels to yield a low GKI. In order to calculate the GKI, blood glucose levels (mg/dL) are divided by 18 and the total is then further divided by ketone levels (mmol/L). This equation is GKI = (blood glucose ÷ 18) ÷ blood ketones. For example, if blood glucose is 96 and blood ketones are 1.5, the GKI would be (96/18)/1.5 or 3.5. In an email to me, Dr. Seyfried mentioned that a GKI as close to 1.0 as possible would be optimal for therapeutic efficacy. His research had mostly been on brain cancer, the most aggressive of cancers. My experience, though, was that a 1.0 or lower GKI was hard to maintain unless fasting or on a drastically restricted diet consisting mostly of fat. I was, however, able to maintain a GKI of 2.0–3.0 more easily, which was still therapeutically effective for my situation.

I ordered Miriam's book and was encouraged to see that she worked with those who had a cancer diagnosis. I knew I would need support, especially in the beginning while I was getting adjusted to therapeutic levels of the ketogenic diet. Miriam and her team helped me to equip myself with the tools I needed to track my nutrients. She also recommended that I use a continuous glucose monitor (CGM) to see what meals did to my blood sugar in real time. A prescription is required to get a CGM in the United States, so I contacted my general practitioner (GP) physician to request one. Typically, CGMs are prescribed by endocrinologists for diabetes but not for cancer.

My GP was aware of my health status, and when I told him that I was declining chemotherapy in favor of a metabolic approach, he strongly advised against this decision. Conventional healthcare practitioners will likely not understand when a patient denies standard protocol, so you have to be prepared for this response. I still needed my GP and wanted to keep him as part of my healthcare team, so I explained my decision, but he refused my request. I was disappointed and wondered if I would need to travel to Canada where CGMs are sold over the counter. After further reflection, I realized that he may have said no because insurance wouldn't cover the CGM, so I contacted him again and explained that I would pay for it out of pocket and that it would help me monitor my ketogenic dietary therapy. I also added that I couldn't travel to Canada in my condition to purchase one. This time he agreed, and the CGM arrived a few days later. If you run into the same situation, find out what your physician's objections are (typically insurance or liability concerns) and see if you can address them. My GP has actually been a helpful member of my healthcare team, so I recommend maintaining your relationships with

The Body

conventional practitioners because healing really does take a village.

Miriam put me on a 1.2:1 ratio of fats to carbohydrates and proteins per meal with proteins not to exceed 30 grams per meal. This meant that roughly 70% of my calories per meal would come from fats (unsaturated, healthy fats, not saturated ones), 20% from protein, and 10% from carbohydrates. In order to put metabolic pressure on cancer cells, a low protein and carbohydrate intake is necessary. Low protein, however, doesn't mean inadequate protein, because I still needed sufficient protein to prevent muscle mass deterioration. Practically, a sample meal looked like eggs cooked in butter or coconut oil, olives, an avocado, MCT oil, macadamia nut butter, and kale. Each meal consisted of a protein (fat-heavy protein like wild-caught salmon, sardines, mackerel, or free-range eggs), cruciferous or low-carb vegetable, and other unsaturated fats. All fruits, grains, legumes, dairy, and hidden sugars in condiments were banned until I was more acclimated to the diet. Counting calories wasn't important, but because I was trying to gain weight and reach 125 lbs (56 kgs), I needed to eat between 1800–2000 calories per day. This was challenging at first because I naturally wanted to only eat about 1000 calories per day. At that rate, however, I would continue to lose weight, which I could not afford post-surgery. Weight loss naturally occurs on a ketogenic diet, so I needed to gain

61

extra weight to compensate for weight loss that would occur over time on the diet.

I began to weigh everything I ate in grams and recorded that information into Cronometer, a nutrition-tracking application. There was a bit of a learning curve with Cronometer, but after that, I found it to be an invaluable tool for monitoring macronutrient (fats, proteins, carbohydrates) and micronutrient (vitamins and minerals) intake. Cronometer utilizes the Nutrition Coordinating Center Food & Nutrient Database (NCCDB) as well as the United States Department of Agriculture National Nutrient Database for Standard Reference (USDA SR28) for extensive and accurate nutritional data.[98] I also liked the ability to create custom recipes in the application, because once you start on this diet, you inevitably learn how to cook other ketogenic recipes for variety's sake. A ketogenic diet is not restrictive in the conventional sense as you typically eat rich, savory food, but being a creature of habit, I needed to learn how to cook new ketogenic meals. I tried to learn at least one new recipe a week and incorporate it into the rotation. One of the cookbooks I recommend is *The Ketogenic Kitchen* by Domini Kemp and Patricia Daly, both cancer survivors.

It was challenging to transition to a high-fat diet because I wasn't accustomed to fat being the majority of each meal. Like most Americans, carbohydrates usually ruled for me, so I felt as if I had turned my diet upside down. I experimented with different types of unsaturated fats to train my body to get used to the new diet. The adjustment took time and didn't occur in just a few weeks. Additionally, I had to forgo fruit entirely. I could let go of sugar (sucrose) without much trouble, but I found myself craving a juicy piece of fruit. After a few weeks, though, I grew more confident that I could eat a ketogenic diet long term.

Working with a Naturopathic Doctor

Before I was diagnosed with cancer, I had started working with a naturopathic doctor who did functional medicine. Naturopathic physicians (NDs) focus on discovering the underlying causes of disease rather than just treating or suppressing symptoms.[99] They are trained in biomedical and diagnostic sciences just like conventional doctors (MDs). They can also order laboratory tests to diagnose the root cause of an illness; laboratory testing is typically more detailed than in conventional care. Rather than using prescription medications to treat illnesses, they use botanical medicine to strengthen weakened immune systems and restore balance. Naturopathic doctors cannot prescribe drugs, however, and will refer patients to MDs when more invasive treatment is necessary. Depending on your insurance, these services may or may not be covered. But if you have a flexible spending account (FSA) or

Health Savings Account (HSA), you may be able to cover most expenses minus supplements. In any case, if you are frustrated with conventional care for a chronic health problem, I highly recommend seeking out a naturopathic doctor. For those without an ND nearby, most naturopaths consult with patients through online video conferencing, so you can be anywhere in the world and still receive care. If your ND orders lab work, you can do those locally at a diagnostic lab close to you or via kits through the mail.

I was working with my ND to address my gut health primarily, but she identified other issues that contributed to my health problems. When you work with an ND, you'll be required to submit a detailed health and medical history prior to the first consultation. As onerous as this can be, it's a useful exercise because you see your health patterns over time, and issues that you thought were unrelated may have actually colluded in facilitating imbalances in the body and mind over time. I started to see that I had had stomach issues since my teenage years and that there was a long pattern of issues affecting my gut microbiome. I had barely started with my ND when I was diagnosed with cancer, so further work with her was held off until later. However, I had completed a full gastrointestinal map (GI map) through DNA stool analysis, a zonulin family protein (ZFP) test for leaky gut syndrome, and a small intestinal bacterial overgrowth (SIBO) lactulose test. While I was recovering from surgery, I was able to have a follow-up consultation with my ND and get those results. Although I was dealing with a more critical problem in cancer, I still needed to address gut issues. Test results indicated that H. pylori had become active again. I did not have any parasites, viruses, yeast infections, leaky gut, or SIBO, but I was low on two strands of beneficial bacteria.

My ND recommended several supplements not only for gut issues but also to help strengthen my immune system, and my kitchen table started to look like a natural pharmacy. I was taking pyloricil, turkey tail, berberine, turmeric, green tea, modified citrus pectin, a multivitamin, digestive enzymes, coenzyme Q10, vitamin D3 with K2, fish oil, probiotics, and acetyl l-carnitine, among others. I had never taken so many capsules in my entire life! Additionally, I was drinking a cup of Alaskan chaga mushroom tea made from conks (woody growth on tree) twice daily. Chaga grows on birch trees and is widely used in traditional medicine. A family friend had bought a bag of chaga conks for me, and my mother pulverized a piece daily to make fresh-brewed tea. At first, the tea tasted bitter, but after a while, I grew accustomed to the taste and began to enjoy it. I could sense how beneficial it was because my body felt good after drinking it. Recent research has indicated that chaga produced cellular damage in cancer cells in vitro and suppressed tumor growth in mice.[100-101]

Supplements for Cancer Prevention

I also want to highlight a few more supplements. The first one is modified citrus pectin (MCP). MCP is derived from citrus peels and pulps, which is further modified by high pH and temperature to delay several stages in the metabolic pathway of cancer cells.[102] MCP arrests tumor cells from attaching to each other or to blood vessel walls to prevent spreading and holds promise as an anti-metastatic supplement. I learned about MCP from Miriam and found that it wasn't contraindicated for ovarian cancer.[103] The MCP I used was Pectasol C in powder form from Econugenics. In hindsight, I would recommend the capsule form instead since the powder is not completely soluble in water and tends to clump at the bottom. If you have sensitive teeth as I do, the citrus can wear away at the enamel.

Another valuable supplement I want to emphasize is green tea, which has been noted to be effective in cancer prevention.[104-105] It is also an effective agent for treating inflammation, high blood pressure, oxidation, and cholesterol. Its anti-cancer effect comes from *catechins*, phenolic compounds that have strong antioxidant actions. Epigallocatechin gallate (EGCG) is the most abundant catechin in green tea and the most effective one for chemoprevention in vitro.[106] I am sensitive to caffeine and normally don't drink it, but I could drink a cup of matcha, young green tea leaves ground into powder, and reuse the tea bag all day long without feeling wired or disrupting my sleep. Plus, the taste and smell of matcha is wonderful. Matcha is bright green, and just by looking at it, I could feel its vibrancy. The brand I like comes from Traditional Medicinals. One note of caution on tea bags: most tea bags are bleached during the manufacturing process, so try to find a brand that uses bleach-free bags. When bleach comes into direct contact with body tissues, especially sensitive ones like the eyes or respiratory tissues, it can cause irritation and cell death.[107] For those living with cancer or having undergone chemotherapy or radiation treatment, decreasing inflammation and toxicity is paramount.

Berberine is another supplement that needs to be highlighted for its preventative effects. I began taking berberine after a consultation with Miriam to lower blood sugar levels. Berberine, which comes from plants in the genus *Berberis*, has a long history of use in traditional medicine for everything from asthma, heart disease, diabetes, eye diseases, skin diseases, ulcers, and urinary problems.[108] Some plants that contain berberine include goldenseal, Oregon grape, bayberry, coptis, and tree turmeric.[109] There is a growing body of research on the multiple-target effects of beberine indicating its efficacy against cancer in cell lines.[110-111] Berberine, like fenbendazole, is insoluble in liquids, so it should be taken with fats. I took both of these medications with a tablespoon of macadamia nut butter and had no side effects. Nanotechnology, which manipulates matter at nanoscopically small scales, has emerged as the main approach to increasing the bioavailability of berberine.[112]

Turmeric is another powerful nutraceutical. Turmeric is a rhizome plant in the ginger family and is used as a spice in Indian and other cuisines. It looks like ginger root but is bright orange. Curcuminoids are bioactive (biologically active) compounds in turmeric with curcumin being the most plentiful. In a few clinical studies, curcumin accelerated tumor cell apoptosis and upregulated p53 molecules in colorectal patients, reduced radiodermatitis in breast cancer patients, and provided relief in patients with external cancer lesions.[113] Taken alone, curcumin is not associated with side effects and is well tolerated, but there are several drug interactions with curcumin, so these should be checked prior to taking it. Curcumin is another herbal supplement that isn't readily bioavailable (insolubility and low absorption), but when taken with piperine, an alkaloid in black and long pepper plants, its bioavailability increases 20 times.[114]

Another supplement I want to highlight is cod liver oil (CLO). CLO is associated with reduced risk of death in lung cancer patients and increased survival in cancer patients with solid tumors.[115] The brand I use is Carlson's Wild Norwegian Cod Liver Oil with vitamins A and D3. This combination has helped me fortify my low vitamin D levels. I also found fish oil supplementation to be a great way to increase unsaturated dietary fats on the ketogenic diet. Anti-cancer properties of omega-3 poly-unsaturated fatty acids (ω3-PUFAs) and vitamin D have been well documented, but their synergistic effect may produce greater efficacy for prevention and potential treatment of cancer.[116]

Regarding vitamin D, supplementation is recommended as an estimated 1 billion people worldwide are deficient.[117] Although the ideal is producing vitamin D through sunlight exposure via the skin, the feasibility of getting enough vitamin D naturally is low and depends on many factors such as latitude, timing, seasonality, the environment, climate, and lifestyle. Those who live in latitudes between 35°N and 35°S for northern and southern hemispheres respectively will get sunlight year-round; those who live above or below these latitudes will not get enough sunlight to produce vitamin D during winter months.[118-120]

Vitamin D Production and Sunlight Exposure During Peak Hours

There are two ultraviolet (UV) wavelengths that penetrate the earth's atmosphere: UVA and UVB.[121] When UVB penetrates the skin, it converts to 7-dehydrocholesterol, then to a pre-vitamin D, and then to vitamin D.[122] In a study based in Riyadh, Saudi Arabia, peak pre-vitamin D hours were from 9:00 am to 10:30 am and 2:00 pm to 3:00 pm during the summer and 10:00 am to 2:00 pm in the winter.[123] Considering the challenges to get adequate sunlight exposure during peak vitamin D production hours, and due to vitamin D's crucial role in calcium homeostasis, supplementation is highly recommended.[124] Research on the association (not cause) between ultraviolet B radiation (UVB) and cancer has indicated higher rates of cancer for those living further away from the equator.[125]

After being on the ketogenic diet for a few weeks, I realized that I needed to swap out kitchen supplies and cookware. For example, I wanted to stop using plastic bags and food storage containers that leached DEHP or di(2-ethylhexyl)phthalate.[126] I replaced them with air-tight glass containers to store food in the refrigerator. I also realized that the nonstick (Teflon-coated) cookware I was using could leach toxic perfluorooctanoic acid (PFOA) into food, and even though this was likely not at harmful levels, research had associated such exposure with increased rates of cancer in animals.[127] I did not want to take any chances, so I began researching cookware that didn't have PFOAs,

PTFEs (fluorinated plastic coating), glues, polymers, coatings or dyes. Stainless steel and cast-iron cookware were better choices than aluminum or copper,[128] but they could still leach metals into food at high temperatures (though producing beneficial effects for vegetarians with iron deficiency).[129] I finally found Xtrema "pure ceramic" cookware and was reassured that it was free of glues, dyes, polymers, lead, cadmium, heavy metals, PFOA, and PTFE. It was more expensive than most cookware but well worth the price considering the quality and longevity. Since I was putting great effort into ensuring proper nutrition and a high quality of ingredients, I also wanted cookware I could trust for daily use.

Challenges on the Ketogenic Diet

Shifting to a ketogenic diet created other challenges for me. One was constipation. I had always been regular with daily bowel movements, but after being on the ketogenic diet for a month, this changed to once every two days and sometimes even three days, which made me feel miserable. Therapeutic levels of the ketogenic diet necessitate low, moderate, and high levels of carbohydrates, protein, and fats, respectively. Fats and proteins are mostly digested by the body, so there isn't much bulk left to excrete as stool. Carbohydrates, however, are the main source of fiber in the diet which, along with water, is necessary for smooth bowel function.[130] I was drinking about 8 cups of water daily, so I knew the constipation wasn't from lack of water. The transit time through the large intestine was taking longer than before and resulted in drier and sometimes impacted stools. It was extremely difficult to pass these bumpy, pebble-like stools.

One thing that worked well was oil enemas or suppositories. There is an Ayurvedic detoxification treatment called Panchakarma that uses herbal medicated oil enemas to release excess air (wind) in the body. I purchased organic sesame oil from Banyan Botanicals and a silicone enema kit and self-administered my suppository with great success. However, this was not a long-term solution. Sesame oil enemas had increased my ketone levels, while OTC glycerin-based (sugar alcohol carbohydrate) enemas escalated my blood sugar levels. I needed to experiment with increasing my fiber while keeping carbohydrates very low, so I introduced a high fiber but low carb vegetable (broccoli, cauliflower, cabbage, green beans, asparagus) at every meal and confined my carb allotment accordingly. I also stopped eating large quantities of macadamia nuts in one sitting. A few at a time were fine, but too many at once seemed to cause constipation. These dietary changes worked well, and I started having a bowel movement every 24 to 30 hours.

Another challenge I faced was transitioning to eating meat. I struggled with the ethics of it and felt guilty about killing animals for nutrition. I kept thinking about Gandhi's teachings that a society's treatment of its weakest members (animals) reveals how evolved it is, and that humans, being stronger, should protect animals. I also knew that I benefitted from cancer research conducted on animals. It was difficult to reconcile the harming and killing of animals, especially when every living being has a fundamental right to life like the rest of us. The best I could do to reconcile this conflict was to buy meat with high levels of animal welfare. If I was going to eat meat, at least I could support farmers whose animals lived in small, local, natural environments instead of mass factory-farmed ones. I learned it was important to ask about welfare labels because, in some cases, "organic" wasn't necessarily better for animals than "local." For example, some organic chickens were fed an organic diet without growth hormones or antibiotics, but they were kept inside their entire lives. That can't be healthy. Other local chickens may not have been raised on organic feed but lived naturally outdoors most of the time, an important consideration.

Working with Conventional and Integrative Practitioners

A few days before my next appointment with my oncologic gynecologist, I heard my inner voice say that the cancer was gone. I was reassured by the message and hopeful that everything would be fine. At the appointment, I had the vaginal cuff checked to make sure it was healing well. It had been about two months since the surgery, and I had informed my oncologist and the nurses that I wasn't going to do chemotherapy. I had expected my doctor to be disapproving, and while she didn't agree with my decision, she accepted it and told me I would be put on a quarterly monitoring plan moving forward. I was happy to hear this because I still wanted her to be part of my healthcare team. She ordered another CA-125 lab test which measures the protein CA-125, a tumor marker in the blood. High CA-125 levels do not always mean you have cancer, however, because they could result from fibroids, menstruation, or other noncancerous conditions.[131] It is thus not accurate enough to screen for ovarian cancer. However, if you've been diagnosed with ovarian cancer, decreasing values signify that a treatment is working and increasing values signify the opposite. My results on this follow-up appointment date were phenomenal! Pre-surgery, my antigen level was 484 U/mL (units per milliliter); post-surgery, it was 243 U/

mL; on the day of my follow-up, it had dropped to 14 U/
mL. A normal value is 35 U/mL or lower. I had been on the
ketogenic diet and fenbendazole for five weeks, so I knew
the metabolic approach was working. I was elated and so
grateful for everything: trusting my intuition, Dr. Seyfried's
research, Miriam's nutritional support, Joe Tippen's blog,
and support from my personal and work communities.
I shared the wonderful news with my friends and family
who were relieved and happy.

During one of my online appointments with Miriam,
she recommended that I consider oncological supervision
with integrative doctors who treat cancer patients with a
metabolic approach. I had already been debating whether to
start oncological supervision with the Care Oncology Clinic
(COC) and visited their website several times. Although
my antigen levels were normal, it was still early, and getting
extra support *would* be a good idea. I contacted the clinic and
had my first online appointment with my new integrative
oncologist a few weeks later. COC uses a combination of
four medications (metformin, atorvastatin, mebendazole,
doxycycline) to treat gynecological cancers.[132] Each one
targets multiple cancer pathways individually, while in
combination, their synergistic anti-cancer effectiveness
increases. Metformin, a commonly prescribed medication
for type 2 diabetes, inhibits cancer cell growth, blocks PARP
enzymes in cells that repair damaged DNA in cancer cells, and

enhances chemotherapy.[133,134] Statins such as atorvastatin, for high cholesterol and heart conditions, sensitize ovarian cancer cells to chemotherapy treatments and reduce cancer-related mortality rates.[135,136] Mebendezole, the anti-parasitic, has been mentioned previously as a repurposed drug for cancer that was found to suppress cancer cell line growth.[137-139] Doxycycline is a common antibiotic that targets cancer stem cells responsible for relapse and blocks MMP molecules that assist in metastasis.[140,141] According to the COC, these medications also modulate protein pathways that support cancer's survival, disrupt cancer cells' signaling activity, inhibit tumor cells' vasculature, target cancer stem cells, reduce glucose and lipoproteins, and strengthen the immune system.[142]

After the initial COC appointment, my oncologist ordered bloodwork that I could do locally. Meanwhile, my new protocol medications arrived in the mail. I was advised to stop taking febendezole, berberine, and coenzyme Q to avoid any drug interactions with the new protocol. I started with mebendezole for a few days and then added metformin and the others one at a time on a set schedule. Initially, I did fine on mebendezole, but a day after adding metformin, I had horrible leg cramps—so painful that they woke me up from sleeping. I also started feeling dizzy and had blurred vision. After contacting COC, they advised me to adjust the medication dose, but I still had problems with the lower dose. I discontinued the metformin to see how I would do without it and added berberine as a substitute for the metformin. The leg cramps and dizziness went away but I was still having blurred vision. I had a gut feeling that the mebendazole was bothering me, so I stopped taking it and switched back to the fenbendazole. My blurred vision improved. This entire calibration process took about three weeks to test out. At that point, I realized that I shouldn't start the COC protocol until the next CA-125 test; otherwise, I wouldn't know if the results were from the ketogenic diet, fenbendazole, and supplement approach I had been doing or the new COC protocol. Plus, I was having such a hard time transitioning to the COC protocol. This turned out to be a good decision as I didn't go back to COC and didn't really need this additional support. Too bad I had to unnecessarily spend a lot of money to figure this out.

My next antigen test was only a month away, so I decided to stay with my prior approach until then. I figured if the numbers stayed low, I would try the next three months on the ketogenic diet with supplements but without the fenbendazole. I hoped to progressively wean myself off as many medications and supplements as I could over time. Once you've had cancer, quarterly follow-ups are necessary, and I figured I would be monitoring cancer antigens (along with hpylori) for several years. I was hopeful that I would continue to show normal antigen levels with each quarterly evaluation, and that I could reduce my treatment protocol until the diet alone with intermittent fasting was sufficient. Other factors like exercise, sleep, stress reduction, and joy were paramount as well.

At the next quarterly CA-125 test, my antigen levels went down even further to 6 U/mL, which was an excellent sign. It indicated that the treatment was working, and I knew it wasn't due to the Care Oncology drugs but to the combination of the therapeutic ketogenic diet, fenbendazole, and surgery. I asked my conventional oncologist about the decreasing antigen levels because I wanted to hear what she had to say about my progress. I was secretly hoping she'd admit that standard treatment was not the only way forward, but all she said was, "Oh, it will never go down to zero," as she hurriedly left the room. There was no empathy or encouragement. Foolish me for hoping for some acknowledgement from a presumably brilliant, classically trained oncologist! I didn't expect her to be knowledgeable in alternative treatments, but physicians should be trained on how to work together with patients to reach their therapeutic goals if they don't choose standard treatment.

During the next quarter, I wanted to see what raising my carb levels would do, so for three months, I occasionally ate white rice, bread, pizza, maple syrup, and mangos, one of the sweetest fruits. I still ate a predominantly whole food diet but with a much higher carb allotment. I was relieved when the next CA-125 test indicated that my antigen levels had dropped even lower to 4 U/mL. I started to realize that I could maintain a healthy, therapeutic regimen by simply eating a whole food, organic diet with an occasional cheat day dining out with friends. It was nice to finally be eating a wider range of fruits and a varied diet.

Another reason I wanted to change my diet was because my stools were still dry, even though I was drinking sufficient water. However, I started to get intuitions that I needed to be careful and maintain a low carb-diet, so I went back to lower levels. Increasing carb levels is a slippery slope that can derail your recovery efforts, so it's better to firmly establish low-carb habits for life. I recommend reading Dr. David Perlmutter and Kristen Loberg's *Grain Brain* to understand how critical a low-carbohydrate diet is for all kinds of ailments including cancer as well as to improve brain health. And even though my test results showed no outward evidence of cancer, I knew I would be monitoring blood levels for the rest of my life. Another CT scan nine months after my surgery also showed no evidence of cancer or metastasis. Hallelujah!

During this time, I started to work with my naturopath again to support overall systemic health. She recommended that I start the Cellcore Biosciences protocol to improve mitochondrial, digestive, and immune system health. I then began a ten-month program of supplements that consisted of five phases: Phase 1) energy and drainage; Phase 2) gut and immune support; Phase 3) whole body immune support; Phase 4) systemic detox; and Phase 5) deeper immune support.[143] The foundational idea behind the protocol is to bring cellular, tissue, and organ function back to a baseline or homeostasis. Cellcore Bioscience's protocol is a roadmap to health that helps minimize reactions from detoxification while effectively removing toxins, parasites, candida, bacteria, viruses, mold, carcinogens, radiation, heavy metals, and so on. If the body's drainage pathways aren't properly opened before starting a detoxification protocol, elimination reactions can make a person feel miserable. For example, if tasked with renovating a hoarder's house that is filled with debris, mold, furniture, rotting food, and trash, you would want to remove it all before attempting to fix up the house. Painting over moldy walls would create all sorts of problems later on even if they looked better initially. Similarly, before addressing illnesses, the first step is to bring the body back into homeostasis by opening up drainage pathways for toxins to pass through.

Cellcore Biosciences uses a bioactive carbon technology (CT) extracted from humic and fulvic acids, naturally modifying them to make them more powerful.[144] CT uses covalent bonds—the strongest bonds in chemistry—to bind onto chemicals, but the difference is that CT is highly "energized." In order for a molecule to enter the body, it has to make it through the stomach acid intact. For example, if you take an herbal supplement to support liver function, only a small portion will actually be absorbed. Most of the herb gets torn apart in the highly acidic environment of the stomach. CT helps buffer the herb, so it passes through the stomach undamaged and enters the small intestine. It has to be small enough to get into the body, and once in, it must pass the gut barrier undamaged, have enough energy to do its job, and be able to get back out. Unlike other toxin binders like charcoal or clay that have no energy (spent energy), CT has enough energy from small, medium, and long-chain carbons to reach the part of the body it needs to go to, perform its binding function, and still have enough energy to carry toxins out of the body.

Prior to CT, individuals could only do detoxification protocols for a few days using binders like bentonite clay or activated charcoal because toxins would get stirred up but not fully removed if drainage pathways weren't opened. They would then be circulating in the body and cause great discomfort. I've experienced these symptoms throughout my life on different cleansing protocols. The advance of CT now allows people to progress more quickly to homeostasis while cleansing with less symptoms. After being on Cellcores's protocol for one month, I noticed a significant improvement in constipation, hot flashes, and hair loss from the trauma of surgery. After three more months, labial itching—a condition I had had for four years went away completely! I feel as if my body is gradually returning to baseline, and I anticipate further improvements as I continue the protocol.

Chapter 2: The Mind

In this section, I share how my mental patterns (thinking) contributed to the development of, and my recovery from, cancer. Healing from cancer is not solely a physical process. The mental aspect is an equally significant part of healing because mind, body, and soul are interconnected. Although the initial focus is on the body after diagnosis, the mind can either facilitate or thwart the healing process long-term. It works in tandem with the body to create wellness (balance) or disease (imbalance). I will be presenting concepts in this section that may not be familiar to some readers such as past life memories (patterns of thinking) that affected my present life. In order to understand this section more fully, I direct readers to the appendices for explanations of Hindu philosophical concepts such the process of manifestation (creation), the definition of mind as an evolute (evolving out of) of creation, and an explanation of karma.

In order to understand the topic of this section: the mind, it must be defined. I have never found such a coherent definition of what the mind actually is than in Indian philosophies. Furthermore, this definition of mind aligns with my actual experience of transcending the mind and returning to it—the back and forth further delineating the boundaries of the mind. Because I didn't want to break up the flow of my personal story, I appended this theoretical knowledge so readers can delve more deeply into the philosophical underpinnings of my narrative should they desire further explanation. I encourage readers to peruse the appendices to really understand what the mind is and how it functions.

My Mental Conditioning

Before I present the mental themes that contributed to my disease and recovery, I want to be clear about something: I am not implying that people with cancer should be blamed for getting it. Assigning self-blame is unproductive and antithetical to healing. Life is replete with challenges for everyone, and all of us have different experiences that we frame in various ways. Even identical twins who grow up in the same environment experience their lives differently. One person gets cancer and transforms while another fails an exam and commits suicide. We all have different mental conditioning which affects how we perceive our lives and behave. Instead of blaming people for their problems, my intention is to emphasize a return to the healing power of integration or wholeness. The more we realize that we aren't hostage to a constantly changing nature but are one with a Consciousness that is whole and eternal, the greater our ability to take positive steps toward healing.

My Spiritual Background

During my recovery process, I reflected on how my mental conditioning contributed to the overall imbalance in my life. One of the strongest mental patterns I had was saying no to life other than meeting my most basic needs. I was more concerned with my inner life (mind and soul). Gradually, however, I became increasingly imbalanced at the expense of outer life (the material world and body). I was 52 when I was diagnosed with cancer, but during my late 20s, I had started becoming more interested in spiritual life, and by age 30, I was actively cultivating it and identifying with it. I explored various alternative and New Age ideas, and then settled into a graduate program at the California Institute of Integral Studies (CIIS) in a comparative Asian religions and philosophies master's program. The program anchored me in traditional ancient knowledge about life's most existential questions. I was always philosophical—even as a young child—though I didn't express it much. It was more of a lived inner experience of the Witness that I was only vaguely aware of. I often felt distanced from the events around me even while participating in them. It was as if some part of my wisdom aligned more strongly with my inner Observer. Although I grew up in a Christian family (my parents even founded a church), I wasn't drawn to Christianity. Instead, I was attracted to freedom. I had a strong desire to be free from the material world though I couldn't articulate it as such during childhood.

Kundalini Support

During my time at CIIS, I attended a talk on kundalini given by Dr. Joan Harrigan, a renunciate who had taken formal vows of abstinence and dedication to spiritual life. She represented Patanjali Kundalini Yoga Care (PKYC), a spiritual guidance service that specializes in supporting individuals in active process towards integration and transformation. Kundalini is the Creative, Active Power that births all phenomena and is the most subtle of all manifestations. Contrary to the latent, passive, undifferentiated Consciousness, she (Kundalini) is the potent, active form of all creation, from the most subtle (spiritual) to the most gross (physical).[1] Kundalini is the Prakriti (Unmanifest Matter) to Purusha (Consciousness). (See Appendix A for more on Consciousness and Unmanifest Matter.) When Consciousness and Unmanifest Matter unite, all of creation (manifest, active matter) unfolds. Active matter is kundalini appearing as various qualities, faculties, and subtle and physical elements. Essentially, kundalini is the source of creative power in the entire universe that includes all living beings. An "active kundalini process" means that kundalini, the animating Force or Power behind all phenomena, has awakened at the base of the subtle body spine (not physical spine) and has begun the ascent through all the chakras (transducers of vital, subtle energy) to the crown of the head. PKYC, based in India (PKYC India) and Austria, is now directed by Silvia Eberl, the authorized lineage holder of this ancient knowledge. If you think you are in a kundalini process and need support, I highly recommend contacting Silviaji (adding "ji" at the end of a name denotes respect) at PKYC India.[2]

After attending the talk on kundalini, I knew I needed guidance from PKYC. I had been having some dramatic effects of a blocked kundalini process and recognized my experiences in Dr. Harrigan's explanations. I started working with PKYC and met my spiritual teacher, Swami Chandrasekharanand (Swamiji), who was a kundalini master and the PKYC lineage holder prior to his death in 2017. Through my years of working with Swamiji, my kundalini process improved, and by age 40, I had turned completely inward and found myself completely withdrawing from the outside world. This occurred not because anything was particularly negative in my life but because spiritual life had deepened to an extent where the serene joy that I felt in absorption was profoundly appealing. My singular goal was spiritual life. I started to focus more on supporting that life, which for me meant living alone, living contemplatively, socializing minimally, working enough but not too much, and living a simple life. I lost interest in worldly affairs, relationships, consumption, and ambition. While my work colleagues were focused on advancing their careers, I had no interest in that. I simply wanted to spend time meditating, contemplating, and reading scriptures while maintaining a good enough outer life to meet my needs. Work was particularly challenging for me, but my teacher had always emphasized that a stable external life was critical to supporting one's spiritual life and that I needed to be self-sufficient and responsible. Still, I had essentially become a lay monastic whose feet were in the world but whose heart was not.

Saying No to External Life

During this period, I would sometimes weep because I did not want to be in the world. I wasn't depressed or suicidal, and there was nothing horrible that I was trying to escape from, and yet I was ready to go. The outside world paled in comparison to the profound peace of absorption. The experience of transcending the mind but then returning to it revealed an indescribable and undesirable contrast, and so I wanted to remain in Oneness. I had no interest in dying and coming back in another incarnation but wanted to be absorbed back into Consciousness, never to return—the ultimate liberation, the final return home. (See Appendix C for more on karma and rebirth.)

I believe that my saying no to external life and the physical world was one of the main mental patterns that laid the conditions for cancer to develop. Along with losing interest in outer life, I also neglected my physical body, and imbalances gradually occurred over many years. At work, I would sit in front of a computer most days for hours at a time and then sit on the meditation cushion at home. My body needed more movement and activity, but I didn't do much of anything other than taking walks. Movement and deep breathing massages the internal organs, but when you are sitting all the time, energy and blood don't circulate sufficiently. So as my meditation practice deepened, that inner stillness was affecting my physical body as well. When the mind grows still, breathing slows down, the parasympathetic nervous system takes over, and sympathetic arousal recedes. Although I wanted to be healthy, I did not pay enough attention to my body and what it really needed: more movement, proper nutrition, and less stress.

The mental pattern of forfeiting outer life for inner

spiritual life in search of liberation is an old one that has been with me through several incarnations. I believe that when we die, the physical body sloughs off, but other nonphysical components (mind and soul) do not. Death occurs at the physical level of the body, while mind and soul continue on to the next body when the time has ripened for it. Nothing is lost in a nihilistic, final sense when we die; it just transforms and appears in another form. The mind carries individual intellect, "I"ness (ego), subtle sensory and motor faculties, and memories to the next incarnation, so mental patterns in this life often have roots in prior incarnations beyond new patterns that are created in the present life. Think of child prodigies with natural skills uncommon for their age and uncultivated during their present lives. Furthermore, there are studies of children who speak about prior incarnations with verifiable facts.[3,4] My belief in reincarnation is not just intellectual or based in faith but also confirmed through my own experience. When the mind becomes more still—when the modifications slow (see Appendix B)—and that stillness stabilizes through repeated experience, past-life memories may emerge as they did for me. Prior to this stage of mental quietude, I did not consciously experience such memories. Instead, I unconsciously experienced the mental patterns of thinking and the feelings associated with them (personality) as just who I was, never questioning why I thought or felt a certain way.

I went through life mostly unaware of my thoughts and feelings and ignorant of their origins because I never intentionally practiced concentration in my younger years. As my meditation practice deepened later in life, past life memories emerged to the point that my mind could catch them. When the mind stays in memory mode without modifying to other modes deep memories may be grasped. Past-life memories may also emerge when the mind is highly focused. For people who have never had such experiences, it is only because they have not developed a focused mind that can be reliably experienced. We are bombarded with constant distractions that stimulate the mind. The only time the mind rests is when we sleep but that is a totally unconscious experience without the light of Consciousness. It is no wonder that deep memories remain hidden. It is challenging to concentrate even for a few seconds without another thought arising. Ironically, concentration is not something we've been taught to do, not even in school. We are told to concentrate on our studies but never taught how to actually concentrate! Unless we purposefully develop this skill, we experience life as the ebb and flow of individual waves. But when we learn to stop the mind's modifications, we realize that we are the ocean itself and not the waves.

Past-Life Patterns

Through meditation, I became aware of some impactful

WHOLE NEW ME

lifetimes where I had conflictedly given up worldly life to pursue spiritual life and liberation from the material world. In one incarnation, I was a priestess in an ancient tradition that utilized sexual spirituality to transcend the mundane and achieve Oneness. Physically, adherents on this path had to undergo mutilation where ovaries were punctured, and breasts were cut off. Sterilization ensured infertility for the priestesses. At the mental level, I had to forfeit marriage, children, and womanhood. These thoughts and feelings made deep grooves in the mind and shaped my present life. I had always been sensitive to physical pain and did not like to see images of surgeries, trauma, or sexual violence. From my priestess memories, I used to have strong vocal kriyas (the release of vital energy in the subtle body to improve energy flow) in my present life where I would scream out from painful memories of this surgery. (Kriyas occur in the subtle body but affect the physical body through the connection between subtle and physical bodies.) I was holding memories of fear and pain in the body of my present life but never considered where those feelings came from. Furthermore, these emotional memories operated in the background. I was also drawn to sisterhood and often wished I had a sister as a child. This affinity developed from some significant lifetimes of priestess and nun-like sisterhood experiences. Interestingly, I attended Wellesley, a women's college, in this life which was the perfect environment for me. I found a close group of friends, and it was an empowering feeling to be surrounded by bright, educated women.

During another lifetime, I was in a horrible marriage devoid of love. My husband behaved badly, telling me I was ugly, couldn't cook, and was horrible in bed. I was deeply hurt by his criticism and cruelty. I later went away to the temple because of it, which is where the seeds of another spiritual life began. One of my most impactful lifetimes was when I lived as a bodhisattva in the Buddhist tradition. A bodhisattva is a person on a path of awakening to unlimited Consciousness (Buddha nature in Buddhism). Bodhisattvas follow ethics and cultivate values (like compassion) not to achieve some ideal but to increase awareness through the process of overcoming suffering.[5] By doing so, bodhisattvas achieve clarity, wisdom, and enlightenment. In Buddhism, suffering in its various forms is the main existential problem for all living beings. Bodhisattvas vow to help others out of their suffering. They learn how to overcome the mind in relation to suffering which results in expanded clarity and compassion. I had experienced a lived understanding of suffering and its hold on the mind, and through the practice of moving out of mental conditioning and toward mental freedom, I developed compassion for, and understanding of, living beings. At the same time, I also felt burdened by having to help others out of suffering. This was yet another life of spiritual training that reinforced a deep longing for release from the material world.

Childhood Yearnings for Freedom

In my present life, I knew I wanted freedom even as a child, but I didn't know where this desire came from. My parents were not oppressive or domineering—quite the opposite—and yet I wanted to be free. They were too busy running their small business to be demanding presences in their children's lives. When we first moved to a new city, we often lived in the back of the store for a few months to save money until we found an apartment. Ignorant of our parents' economic hardships, my brother and I happily played in the back of the store and spent our time building forts out of large cardboard boxes. Trying to make a living, my parents placed most of their attention on the store, and I remember feeling neglected and lonely throughout my childhood and adolescence but unable to express these feelings. At the same time, I needed solitude while growing up. Because I was accustomed to inner quietude from spiritual training in previous lives, I needed my own space and time alone to myself. I kept begging my parents for my own room and was delighted when we moved into our first house with three bedrooms, one of which became mine.

As a child, I knew I didn't want to be married or have children. Most young girls in the 1970s were conditioned to be married and raise a family, but I was adamantly against being a mother and wife. I never thought about why I had such a strong stance against family life; I just felt these feelings and never questioned them. In retrospect, however, it seems odd that a child would have such adverse feelings without serious problems at home. I later realized that these feelings came from grief, self-blame, and anxiety over losing a child in a prior lifetime. These painful memories left me with a revulsion toward having children and family life. As a result, I came into this lifetime longing for freedom from gendered norms and family responsibilities. Being conditioned by the priestess lifetime where a woman's role in spirituality was respected, I struggled in this life with the limitations of Confucian roles that came with being raised in a Korean household.

Korea adopted Confucian ethics and philosophy from China, but in a process spanning several hundred years (1300s–1500s), the Joseon dynasty took Confucianism to unparalleled heights.[6,7] In Confucianism, a woman's role was one of lifelong obedience to men: first to her father, then to her husband and his family, and finally to her son in widowhood. Seeing how hard my mother worked both at the family store and at home triggered deep memories of being an overworked mother and wife stuck in an unfulfilled life and loveless marriage. My mother's daily sacrifices both frustrated and angered me. Being the girl in the family, I helped her with household chores but felt conflicted by it. I thought it was unfair that my brother and father did less work at home but complaining never seemed to change the oppression I felt in the house. I'm not saying that my mother felt oppressed taking care of our family; rather, this is how I viewed the situation due to my previous mental conditioning. We do not see reality as it is; we see it as we are (through our mental filters).

Difficulty Relating to Others

Another deep mental pattern I experienced during this life was difficulty in relationships. I often felt that people were a burden, and that at any moment they would encroach upon my energy and freedom. This was because I had a pattern of not being able to express what I needed in relationships, which left me feeling exhausted, unseen, unloved, and used. Past-life experiences of heavy responsibility, coupled with the inability to express my feelings, made me avoid demanding relationships. Another manifestation of this difficulty in relating to people showed up as inner conflict about helping others. Although I felt fulfilled when helping people, I also felt burdened by it. It took a while to become aware of the reasons behind this inner conflict. During my bodhisattva lifetime, I felt compelled to help others due to the development of compassion through spiritual training. Realizing how all human beings experience misery from attachment, greed, anger, illusion, and so on, compassion naturally arises as awareness expands. Spiritual training was conflated with compassion and clarity, and so through helping others, I felt uplifted. In other lifetimes of marriage, motherhood, and family life, however, I was conditioned to not express my feelings, which created strong mental patterns of frustration, helplessness, exhaustion, and obligation when taking care of others. The inner conflict I experienced in this lifetime about helping people was a combination of these mental patterns. I would feel both happy and overloaded. These strong patterns were overlaid on each other and became the mental backdrop for how I related to people in the present life.

During my recovery process from cancer, I reflected on how this inner conflict of helping others could be completely neutralized just by addressing the real issue: expressing myself. Once I expressed my needs and feelings in relationships (boundaries), I was better able to relate to others. I could also feel joyful again while helping others and not be fearful of draining my energy.

I need to pause here to explain that linking current mental patterns to past-life origins is not my main intention. I discuss it here because it's an important part of my story (background). The real import is to become aware of your own mental conditioning whether you believe in reincarnation or not. You don't need to explore past lives to identify your mental patterns and expand awareness. The mental content of your present life is the main event and where you are now. Simply making time for reflection and contemplation, working with your dreams, or working with a therapist can support greater insight. The main objective is to increase self-awareness by moving beyond limited patterns of thinking.

Another (though secondary) aspect of my mental conditioning when it came to relationships was being afraid to ask others for help. This discomfort was connected to feeling helpless in lifetimes where I worked hard for others without any help and while unable to express my needs. Not used to receiving help, I found it hard to ask for it. Also, being born an Asian female in those lifetimes placed me in societal conditions of low power and deference but with a disproportionately high work burden. Additionally, I developed self-confidence and self-reliance in other lifetimes due to spiritual training, so I also had positive mental patterns of working hard. These various patterns conflated in my mind and created a sense of both helplessness and independence. In my current life, I experienced this inner conflict as not wanting to ask others for help and doing everything myself. By viewing relationships in this way, I was unable to experience self-confidence and the positive feelings that accompany it, but I also didn't feel complete helplessness either. Thankfully, I was still able to be somewhat self-reliant and achieve certain goals, but I also felt that any hard work I undertook would be a solo venture. In that way, these feelings may have limited me from dreaming big dreams that involved working with groups of people. Influenced by past life patterns, I was used to having intense relationships with a few people one-on-one. An astute college friend noticed this when she once remarked that our relationship was intense and focused.

Relationships are critical to self-development (self-awareness) because we learn by relating to others. Achieving goals is also facilitated by relating to others. For example, brainstorming creative ideas is better in groups than thinking them up on your own. Living offers countless opportunities to learn and grow in relationships. Every significant person in your life (even the difficult ones) can teach you more about yourself and help you become more successful. After I was diagnosed with cancer, I realized I needed support and asked my family, friends, and colleagues for help, which wasn't easy to do because I had viewed others as a burden and did not want to be a burden to them. The mental patterns I carried affected not only how I related to others but also how I perceived how they related to me. Mental patterns do not allow you to see others as they are but as who you are, so we continue to have the same feelings in every relationship even though the people change. Although it was uncomfortable, it felt good to ask for help and receive it. The gravity of cancer forced me to do it. I began to notice my heart and head connecting more easily than before. It was a subtle perception yet profoundly healing. In the process of neutralizing this old mental pattern, relating to others also became easier and more natural. I no longer felt discomfort asking for help because I started to express my needs. I started to feel an expanded love in my heart for others as old patterns melted away. This mental healing allowed me to notice who my family and friends really are rather than who I thought them to be (my mental projections). I started to live more in the present moment of relationships rather than through past mental conditioning.

Loss of Joy in Life

Another insight I had about the impact of my prior mental conditioning in the development of cancer was that I had gradually lost all joy in living. Because I was so focused on my internal world at the expense of outer life, my energy followed suit. I didn't pay much attention to anything physical whether it was my body, job, or relationships. For example, I started snacking late at night while watching videos on the internet. During my preteen and teenage years, I spent hours every day watching television. I enjoyed being passively entertained and entering another vista through the screen. As an adult, I didn't watch as much television, and after becoming more spiritually focused, I threw out my TV and spent almost a decade without watching it at all. However, as my disinterest in outer life deepened over time, I started internet surfing at the end of the day. These videos occupied my mind, made me happy, and satisfied my social needs, albeit virtually. I liked socializing to an extent, but I craved alone time and needed people to go away. I wasn't able to offer much time to anyone beyond my immediate family, so most relationships fell away. The internet was something I could turn off whenever I wanted, but relationships required energy and attention. When people like each other, it's natural to spend more time together, and because I didn't want to disappoint or hurt people, I avoided making new friends. I thought, *Why start something that I knew I would not be able to maintain?*

While watching videos at night, I would mindlessly snack and overeat which affected my digestion. I enjoyed the sensation of tasting food and chewing it, but I wasn't listening to my body. Although my stomach was full after dinner, I still snacked while watching videos to feel pleasure, overloading my system with undigested food. This behavior, though physical, came from the mind. My life lacked balance and, over time, the imbalance increased to the point that I lacked any outward joy. To compensate, I developed this harmful habit of snacking that contributed to an unhealthy physical terrain. Life had become a disciplined routine of attending to my spiritually focused inner life, but the profound joy and peace I felt at the spiritual level and understood at the mental level had not fully come down to the physical level. I still had traces of mental patterns that needed dissolution. Even though I'd been aware of these patterns, and they had thinned out over the years, they still weren't fully cleared and obscured my awareness when I was not absorbed in my inner life.

The mental patterns (thoughts and feelings) I have presented here illustrate the karma that had ripened enough to bear fruit in my present life. (See Appendix C.) Their themes became the warp and woof of my life's tapestry. My mental matrix included: saying no to life, desiring freedom from the world, intense inner and spiritual focus, needing solitude, aversion to traditional women's roles, inclination toward sisterhood, antipathy toward marriage, disinterest in family life, difficulty with relationships, seeing people as burdensome, inability to express feelings, compassion for others, being fulfilled by helping others, and lacking joy. I experienced life through these filters, and my actions were driven by attraction to pleasure and avoidance of pain in relation to these filters. As I went through life, I strengthened some of my mental patterns, weakened others, and created new ones. The diagnosis of cancer helped me to further reflect on how these patterns contributed to its development and through this reflective process, my awareness (wholeness) increased.

This healing process allowed me to integrate Consciousness more fully all the way down through the spiritual, mental, and physical levels of selfhood. By connecting back to Wholeness (Love), the essence of being, a subtle but profound healing occurred.

Chapter 3: The Spirit

In this section, I present healing at the spiritual level and how profoundly impactful it was for me even though it's a subtle, imperceptible experience to the physical senses. Spiritual experience can only be perceived with a highly concentrated mind and not with a distracted mind as experienced in wakeful and even dream states. Spiritual activity is also not experienced in deep sleep (unconsciousness) because there is no mind to report the experience. You don't know who you are or that you even have a body in deep sleep. These cycling states of mind (modifications of the mind) – wakefulness, dreaming, and deep sleep—do not typically facilitate the perception of spiritual phenomena. However, if the mind is concentrated during wakefulness, spiritual activity may be perceived. Furthermore, if the mind is concentrated during dream-like states (without rapid eye movement—non-REM), memories of past lives may emerge.

Both wakeful and dreaming spiritual experiences that are produced from a concentrated mind require *interiority* or a withdrawal from the physical and subtle senses. Moving from waking to dreaming to deep sleep states represents a progression towards greater interiority, though it is still a moving cycle that never stops. In order to break free from the continuous cycling of the mind and realize its limitations or boundaries, meditation is necessary. Meditation allows individuals to go beyond the mind's movements and experience the essence of being (Observer or Awareness). When an individual transcends the mind, the limits of the mind become known. It's like thinking that the ocean is the furthest boundary of your country. If you have never gone beyond it, you wouldn't know that another territory exists on the other side. When that experience of the Observer is stabilized with repeated experience, Consciousness expands, and this unlimited Observer is then realized and brought into active awareness. This is emancipation. Life is then experienced with a full-on Observer (Consciousness) even while the mind modulates. (See Appendix B for further explanation on transcending the mind.)

Consider this example: When you look at a garden, the mind shifts (modulates) into different modes such as identifying what you see (perception, processing, correct knowledge), imagining something else while looking at the garden (daydreaming or fantasizing), or remembering a memory associated with the garden. After emancipation occurs, the mind may still modulate as you look at the garden, but you feel as if you are looking at yourself because your "I-making" function (ego) has considerably thinned out and mental modifications are either slowed or the intensity of experience has decreased. Expanded consciousness fills the space previously defined by the ego. There are no more boundaries of selfhood or constant self-referencing. Consciousness itself shines through ubiquitously. Then, you view both external and internal worlds as the Self instead of as separate from you (ego). Prior to that, we remain ignorant that there is something beyond the mind and that the mind is distinct from Consciousness because the mind is constantly cycling. After emancipation, you may also experience pure perception where the mind is not commenting on what it perceives but simply doing the action of perceiving. The mind stays in one mode (perceiving) rather than cycling through the modes. This experience feels like simply being in the present moment—the power of now. It is not fleeting though; the power of the present moment stays with you. A real spiritual transformation occurs—not just the temporary cessation of the mind's movement.

Intuitions About Cancer

A few years prior to my cancer diagnosis, I had an intuitive warning about it. At that time, I thought that the intuition was a sign that H. pylori had become active again and not that cancer had actually developed. After getting an EGD, I learned that I had intestinal metaplasia, an initial condition that could develop into stomach cancer, so I began taking Ayurvedic herbs and altered my diet. Several months later, I retested for H. pylori with a negative result, and a follow-up EGD indicated that the stomach lining had healed. These were my first intuitions about cancer. I mistakenly assumed my intuition was about hpylori, but the cancer was actually on my ovary. Still, these intuitions served as admonitions that focused my mind on observing my health. Without these helpful alerts, my health may have deteriorated even more than it did. Furthermore, I probably would have experienced more anxiety, fear, and stress if these earlier warnings had not prepared me for what was to come.

After I was discharged from the hospital and came home, I couldn't move very well and spent most of my time in bed. Day after day, my external environment grew quieter and more still, mirroring the deep rest I needed to heal from the trauma of surgery. In this deepening repose, I meditated a few times daily and received intuitions that chemotherapy wasn't necessary. Prior to surgery, I prayed that it would be the extent of my treatment. When my oncologist later recommended six rounds of chemotherapy, I felt deflated. After all, intuition had told me that I wouldn't need it, so I was surprised when my oncologist recommended it. I went home disheartened and feeling deeply conflicted. After a few more days had passed, I kept feeling like I should trust the intuitions. Again, when intuition occurs, you immediately trust it because it doesn't come from a distracted mind; it comes from an extremely focused one. (See Appendix D for further discussion of intuition.) It is hard to describe the experience of such a knowing. I call it a knowing because it isn't a feeling or sensation but something else, something "higher." Your inner wisdom recognizes the intuition, and you trust the information or warning. And when you have more than one intuition, it makes you more certain. Had I not had other intuitions about forgoing chemotherapy, I might not have searched for alternative treatments or had the courage to say no to the standard protocol. Intuition was my real compass for finding the path forward. Each successive intuition dropped into my being like a stone in a pond, creating ripples of reinforced thoughts of empowerment. It was intuition that saved me from the damaging effects of chemotherapy and helped me find the road less travelled.

I also received another intuition that led me to finding the alternative treatment I needed. Initially, I knew I did not want to do chemotherapy, but I didn't know what to do instead. Early one morning while meditating, I had an intuition about Boston. I wasn't sure what this meant and wasn't thinking about anything related to Boston, so I simply made a mental note. A few days later, I was on YouTube and found a presentation that Dr. Thomas Seyfried had made on the metabolic approach to cancer. Everything Dr. Seyfried presented made sense to me about cancer being a metabolic disease brought about by malfunctioning, damaged mitochondria, and that by cutting off glucose and glutamine, the main fuel sources for cancer, healing could occur. While viewing the video, I just knew he was right. After learning that he was a researcher at Boston College, I was delighted by the synchronicity. This intuition, along with reviewing his research, furthered my resolve to pursue a metabolic approach to treating cancer.

Without intuition, I would not have been as confident in my search for an alternative to chemotherapy. Perhaps I would not have even tried and just passively accepted my doctor's recommendations due to being overwhelmed—a completely normal response. I cannot emphasize enough the importance of silence and stillness (i.e., reducing distractions) when making life-altering decisions. The process of intuition unfolding through soul, mind, and body takes time, needs space, and should never be rushed.

The Spirit

Each intuition came at the right time for me, and combined with my reasoning mind and inner feelings, a whole-person response emerged. It wasn't logic, fear, or doubt making the decision; it was spirit, heart, and head, working together in an integrated way. I listened to my inner wisdom, which supported me to make the right decision for myself.

The most profound intuition I experienced during my recovery was when I received an intuition that Jesus would come for me. I was surprised by this because I am inclined towards Indian spiritual traditions. Although I know that Jesus is a sacred heart master, healing master, and savior to Christians, I was not actively praying to him or calling on him. By contrast, my mother, who is a sincere Christian, had developed a living relationship with him in her heart. She had been praying that I would follow Jesus for many years, and when I was diagnosed with cancer, her prayers, driven by the unconditional love of a mother for her child, intensified. Mothers have an innate capacity for unconditional love because in their noblest version, they abandon themselves for their children. Their actions aren't taken for their gain but for their children's benefit. It becomes a "two as One" experience. In this capacity, mothers can perform actions without accumulating karma. They are literal hosts for their children who are nourished by them just as Jesus is an unconditional savior or host for humankind.

I was sure it was my mother's prayers to Jesus that caused him to come to me. One morning, in the early hours of stillness while lying in bed with a focused mind, an intuition announced that Jesus had come—not as a form but as a presence. I knew I needed to remain still, and then a rush of extremely subtle energy flowed down from the crown of my head, down my body, to the end of the spine. The presence was one of Pure Love and healing. After the flow subsided, I knew that healing had occurred. After my experience, I also noticed that my heart had opened up and was connecting to my head more easily than before. It was an extremely subtle and sublime experience.

Creativity Returns

One of the lessons from my experience of ovarian cancer was that I needed to bring more joy into my external life. As I contemplated what made me feel joyful, creativity rose to the surface. Ovarian cancer affects a woman's reproductive ability, which is fundamentally about creative power. At the physical level, creative power could look like bringing a fetus to term and birthing a baby. At the mental level, it might be thinking or imagining something novel for the mind to engage in like a project, invention, or artistic work. At the spiritual level, it could be an aspiration to deepen one's practice. Desire is fundamental to development because it's the initial spark of the creative process. Without desire, artists would not create, inventions would not be produced, ideas would not be realized, and babies would not be born. Earlier in my life, I expressed creativity through writing poetry, books, and even screenplays, but as I got older, I found I had lost my creative expression. I had settled into a routine outer life that kept my life stable but lacked creativity. One of the questions I kept asking myself is, "What do I want to spend my time doing?" Whether I lived 1 more year or 20, how did I want to spend my time? If I didn't work, what would I do? I realized that what fed my soul was writing and public speaking, because they allowed me to express ideas and share knowledge. I had literally lost my creative, physical power due to menopause, but it did not mean that I couldn't create anymore. I needed to go to a higher octave to express creativity. So, I started writing again, which brought the creative process back into my life, a process that was deeply healing (Wholeness) and joyful.

My Journey Back Home

When I reflect on my life, I realize that my primary focus was always existential—the desire to be free from a limited existence. When my soul incarnated into this lifetime, it desired freedom, and while working through my mental conditioning (karma), I defined freedom according to the degree of awareness at the time. My soul knew that the freedom I was searching for was liberation from the mind in order to rest in the Observer, but my mind didn't know what that was. Thus, in my younger years, I didn't understand that I needed to go inward to find my soul's true desire, so I searched for freedom externally. Practically, this looked like living where I wanted, doing the work I wanted to do, or studying what interested me. When I found I could transcend my mind, I started to live primarily for my inner life, which led to an imbalance in external life. I had not fully integrated the light of Consciousness down through the mental and physical levels of my individualized awareness (ego), so there were still opaque areas of conditioning that existed.

As humans evolve spiritually, there is a journey toward the light, but then that light must penetrate back down through all the levels of existence until it reaches the physical. True integrated awareness occurs when Consciousness is no longer some lofty goal to reach but exists everywhere one looks. When Consciousness is fully integrated, the entire world becomes Consciousness. Everything you see around you is Consciousness, and you no longer get tricked by the apparent illusion of diversity. It doesn't mean that hardships stop happening. You can still be affected by disease, the environment, the behavior of others, but you no longer ride these difficulties as an individual wave but as the ocean itself. The personal ego becomes greatly thinned, and all phenomena is viewed largely without attachment.

Living becomes more of a pure perceptive experience. The instrument of mind is no longer clouded by personal karma; you have a clear instrument to perceive the world, and that perception is seated in the knowledge of the Seer. Therefore, everywhere you look, you see the Self, Oneness, Wholeness, Consciousness. It is like going through life not as you but as everything. The wave becomes the Ocean.

Spiritual Guidance in Dreams

In the mental section, I described some past lives where I had spiritual training. These experiences left deep existential, karmic patterns in the mind. Throughout my present life, I identified with Indian spiritual traditions on an ego level. My spiritual teacher was Indian, and he taught me this knowledge through his commentary on Indian philosophies which I then applied to my own experience. When these philosophical scriptures are only learned intellectually, there are limitations to understanding, but when you learn and experience them both intellectually and experientially, you internalize the teachings and have a much better understanding. I had existential karma that directed the focus of my present life to be spiritual but also created a mental block. Years before my cancer diagnosis, I had a dream that showed me how to remove this block. An excerpt is included here:

I enter an art room and see ladies painting. I realize it is

not the right room and then enter another room. I see an
old man, my spiritual teacher, there. He is trying to say
something, so I bend over to hear him. He latches onto my
ear intensely, almost like he is going to bite it off. I cannot
hear him, but then, my hearing sharpens. I hear, "Help
me! Help me!" He tells me, "They will try to get you,"
and I know this to mean the Buddhists. I ask him, "What
happens if you change religions?" He shows me the answer
on the wall. I see a mask, but it is turned inward facing
the wall. This terrifies me because it indicates that I will
lose my face. I will have no religious identity. I then tell
my teacher that I was planning to go to my grandmother's
Buddhist temple in Korea, but then I suddenly yell out, "I
want to be a Vedantin. I want to follow Hinduism!" I am
extremely upset and crying as I yell this out. My teacher
then turns a tapestry that was hanging on the wall into a
message that says, "Be in the One." Then he leaves. I feel
intense existential fear, like a soul terror. I am sobbing and
feel a comforting female presence as grief is pouring out of
me. I wake up with my heart pounding.

When I awoke from this dream, profound grief bubbled
up to the surface of awareness. The existential fear I had
felt was palpable and rippled through my psyche, leaving
me feeling terrified. The dream showed me that I held deep
attachments to different religious identities from past lives.
In my Buddhist lifetime, I was attached to helping others
out of suffering even though it wasn't good for me, thus the
"Help Me!", but it would keep me stuck in those past life
patterns. I was unable to find the freedom I so desperately
longed for in the past, and a part of my ego was still stuck

in the same pattern of identifying with yet another spiritual identity in this life (Hinduism). The dream was telling me that I had to go beyond all religions (constructs of the mind) and all phenomena and rest in Consciousness. This was terrifying for me because I was so attached to my religious identity. I had to be in Oneness (Love, Wholeness) itself. At that time, the latent, unconscious energy of these past patterns was still influencing my mind. This dream shined the light of Consciousness onto my deeper internalized memories and emotions. By bringing them up to the surface of awareness, a healing occurred that helped me to integrate these subtle, hidden patterns. I wouldn't find the freedom I desired at the level of the mind when it was focused on existential or religious paths. I needed to go beyond all phenomena no matter how subtle. Real freedom would only be found in Oneness, where Consciousness alone exists.

This dream reminded me of another terrifying existential dream I had even earlier in my life about my soul's deep desire for freedom, seeded from prior lives:

I am inside a large compound and searching for a way out. I open door after door thinking that each door will lead me outside, but I find myself inside another room each time. This happens over and over. I feel exhausted and desperate to leave. Then, I see a way to go out to the courtyard, but even the courtyard, as nice as it is, is just another space that I cannot leave. Finally, I walk into another room and find an Indian man who is holding up a flame, the flame of Vedanta. Something within me knows that this is the

*real way out. He touches me and I feel a surge of energy go
through me and then I awaken.*

This dream may not seem terrifying, but I experienced
it with highly charged feelings of fear and desperation. The
experience felt like a soul terror and not like the common
feeling of personal fear. It reverberated throughout my
psyche and affected me for some time after. It was the first
time I became more conscious of my desire for freedom
from the material world. Occurring many years prior to
meeting my spiritual teacher, the dream showed me that
Oneness was the real way to liberation. Advaita Vedanta is
a non-dualistic philosophy which states that the world is
really One (Consciousness) but appears to be multiple. Just
as my teacher told me to "Be in the One" and not get caught
up in past attachments of the mind to specific religions, he
signaled that message decades prior to even meeting him
in this "escape room" dream! When I was eight years old,
I wrote my first poem ever. Guess the topic of the poem:
reincarnation! I should have known then that I was an old
soul looking for the way out.

Abiding in Oneness—True Unconditional Love

The mind must be transcended to be in Oneness. We can
experience Oneness momentarily through unconditional

love where the self is forgotten, but it is not the same as the long-lasting transformation that occurs with actual liberation from the mind and all its worlds (*lokas*).[1] These existential dreams presented a path to my ultimate spiritual healing. They indicated that resting in the Seer—the eternal Self—would help me to break free from the mind's labels. In recalling them during my recovery, their message made a lot of sense as my experience of healing was one of resting in peace, connectedness, and love. It wasn't necessary to be an adherent of a specific religious or spiritual tradition. It was all about being the Wholeness and bringing that realization into an integrated experience of life.

The Sufi mystic poet Rumi said that everything in the universe was within the individual. As above so below. The macrocosm (universe) is in the microcosm (individual). This realization that all phenomena is within us is conveyed beautifully in his poetic metaphors.

This moment
this LOVE comes to rest in me,
Many beings in one being
In one wheat grain
a thousand sheaf stacks.

Inside the needle's eye
a turning night of stars.
This moment –
This LOVE.[2]

True unconditioned love is experienced when we become one with another soul. When we no longer see ourselves as separate from the other but see two as one, Love reveals itself. Duality gives way to Oneness. The multiple becomes the One. Our true Self is Love, and from that essence, the many (othering or diversity) is created. When we break through the limitations of individual selfhood and realize the unlimited Self, we discover what we truly are. We are able to be Love itself, which has always been the ground of our individual self regardless of how we have misperceived and limited our unchanging essence.

The experience of self-realization is beyond mind and words, so attempts to describe it are futile. That is why poets use metaphors and sages use silence to point toward Self. It is an experience of profound peace, joy, love, silence, stillness, awareness, existence, wholeness, and oneness, all at the same time! Everything is connected in Oneness because everything gets absorbed back into Wholeness. There are no more "parts of the whole." Actually, the parts (phenomena) never existed in an absolute sense although they appeared to exist in a relative one. This is why transcending the mind and resting in Wholeness is profoundly healing and integrating. We return to our spiritual origin, which acts like a reset and exponentially expands beingness into an eternal moment (transcending time, which belongs to the body and mind). For example, people who have had spiritual encounters during near-death experiences come back healed or changed.[3-5] These experiences are not the same as absorption, where the mind is transcended, because phenomena are still experienced, but they reconnect individuals directly to their spiritual power, which is profoundly healing. From a healing perspective, it doesn't really matter whether the doors to spiritual power are opened by prayer, meditation, near-death, or other experiences. What matters is that spirituality is a powerful source of healing that deserves acknowledgement and attention in the healing process. Those living with cancer and any imbalance or disease could benefit greatly from introspection, rest, meditation, and stillness. The inner journey, intentionally traversed, has vast potential for healing.

Conclusion

Remission

One year after my diagnosis, I am in complete remission, which means that all signs and symptoms of cancer have disappeared. Remaining in complete remission for five years or more means that you are likely cured, but cancer cells may still remain in the body and could come back in the future so continued monitoring is necessary. I am on a quarterly monitoring plan which includes blood draws for CA-125 levels and pelvic examinations every three months. My CT scan nine months after surgery also showed no evidence of disease. It is still early in my remission, so I continue to prioritize my health with an attitude of integrating positive, lifelong habits.

I no longer take fenbendazole, but it is good to know that it is available if needed. I keep cancer away through dietary and lifestyle changes. After trying some variations of low-carb diets, I settled into the Paleo diet which is where you eat similar to early humans during the Paleolithic age. This is a diet mostly of fish, meat, vegetables and fruit (mostly berries) and excludes dairy and grains. Our early ancestors were hunter-gatherers not agrarians, so they didn't have access to dairy and grains. Eliminating dairy and grains—inflammatory triggers—has made a huge, positive difference in my health. Practically, a sample meal looks like a salad with protein of choice, a heaping side of cooked vegetables, and unsaturated fats like oils, olives, avocados, and nuts on occasion. In cooler seasons, I switch from salads to cooked vegetables and soups because raw food is cold, harder to digest, and disturbs my constitutional balance. As a rule, I buy all organic, and for meat and seafood, I try to source from as natural and healthy environments as possible. This is typically meat from grass-fed (not grain-fed) animals and wild-caught seafood to reduce exposure to genetically modified organisms (GMOs), antibiotics, hormones, pesticides, and toxins—not to mention animal welfare. It's important to know where your food comes from. For example, wild caught fish isn't always better than farmed fish. You don't know what wild caught fish have been exposed to versus farmed fish who may have been raised with quality practices and fed nutrients without antibiotics. On the flip side though, not all farmed fish operators are equal. Some use antibiotics and chemicals and are not sustainable and eco-friendly. You have to do your homework.

When dining out, I choose restaurants that have options for me and that source locally as much as possible. I can't always control my choices when dining out with loved ones, but I do the best I can given what's available. It's a treat for me to spend time with my friends (a "heart snack"), so connecting with them is my priority rather than the food. At times, while traveling, I have to switch to a low-glycemic diet for a few days instead of Paleo depending on where I am so being flexible is necessary and realistic. Hold things loosely!

I also combine my diet with intermittent fasting to put additional metabolic pressure on any lingering or potential cancer cells. I typically do an 8-hour window of eating with a 16-hour window of fasting. This works out to two meals a day which is usually breakfast at 8:00 am, lunch at 1:00 pm and a snack before 4:00 pm (as needed). If I don't eat a snack, I stop eating by 2:00 pm which gives me a longer fasting period—a 6:18 hour ratio. Sometimes, due to scheduling, I eat lunch and dinner instead without an evening snack for a longer fasting window. I find that eating breakfast and lunch works better than eating lunch and dinner; that way, I don't have as much glucose circulating in my body at night.

I do intermittent fasting daily with an occasional 24 to 72-hour water fast monthly when I don't eat at all but take electrolytes to support hydration and blood pH levels.

I continue to work with my naturopath on strengthening my immune system, improving my microbiome, eliminating toxins, and improving metabolic function. Constipation continues to be a problem for me. Initially, I thought it was due to the ketogenic diet, which definitely contributed to constipation but wasn't the main reason. After changing to a Paleo and low-carb diet, I still had issues. My surgeon had told me that the bowels would fill the space left by the reproductive organs, but she didn't tell me about the injury to the nerves. During a hysterectomy, the pelvic plexus—the intersection of the pelvic parasympathetic and sympathetic nerves—is damaged.[1] The pelvic plexus is responsible for the coordinated movements of the smooth muscle of the bladder and bowel, and during surgery, there are many dissections that result in losing a large portion of these pelvic nerves.[2] Though it is debated whether hysterectomy causes constipation or not,[3-5] I experienced a significant difference pre and post-surgery in bowel function. Prior to the hysterectomy, I never had problems with bowel movements, but even a year after surgery, I continue to have slow motility and constipation. To help address these issues, I started working with a physical therapist to strengthen the pelvic floor and breathe diaphragmatically. A tablespoon of extra virgin, cold-pressed organic olive oil first thing in the morning started to show results after a few weeks, and magnesium citrate, an osmotic laxative, also helped.

Another issue that I am working on is myofascial release of scar tissue (breaking down scar tissue) that formed during surgery. After abdominal surgery when muscles and tissues are cut, the body creates scar tissue as a healing response to surgical trauma. Over time, this scar tissue may adhere to deeper tissue layers and other organs creating problems with blood flow and obstruction. The incision on the surface of my skin was about 18 centimeters long and formed a long, thick, raised scar. The external appearance of the scar offered clues to the condition of internal scarring. I was concerned that If I didn't do something to help break down the scarring, it could create more serious problems later on. Presently, my daily myofascial rituals consist of pelvic massage, finger friction massage on the scar, and heated castor oil packs. These combined actions help improve blood flow to the pelvic region, encourage myofascial release, and promote detoxification.

Cupping therapy with my physical therapist also makes the scarring more pliable (flexible like skin tissue rather than solid scar tissue) and less likely to adhere at deeper tissue layers. Cupping therapy involves placing a cup on the surface of the skin and creating a suction force that lifts up the skin and scar tissue. Cupping promotes blood flow and myofascial release, and it relieves pain in the area being suctioned, even though it may feel uncomfortable if scar tissue is sensitive. Acupuncturists and physical therapists can provide these services, and there are silicone suction cups you can order online for home use.

Overall, my health is a work in progress that is gradually improving. Stretching, muscle strengthening, physical therapy, walking, yoga postures, and meditation are also part of my daily routine. I do all of this at home, so it doesn't require special equipment or time driving to the gym. Ironically, I am becoming healthier than ever before as result of cancer.

Cancer as a Metaphor for Healing

Cancer is a deeply personal experience, and how one thinks of it depends on their perspective. There are pros and cons of conceptualizing cancer as a metaphor.[6-7] Some describe cancer as a battle, such as, "The war against cancer" or "He succumbed to his battle with cancer." People with cancer are often told to fight it, which may or may not be positively motivating depending on the individual. Cancer is also likened to a destructive abnormal growth or infestation as in, "The rat infestation spread like a cancer" or "The city's drug problem has spread like a cancer." It is also referred to as an exhausting journey, as in "She travelled a long road during her recovery from cancer." Describing cancer as a fight, virus, or trial conveys a difficult, devastating, prolonged experience without much hope. These metaphors are violent, oppositional, divisive, and contradictory to wholeness and healing. Cancer's metaphors reveal the entrenched bias of viewing it as primarily a physical disease or experience, so it is predominantly described as a horrible, painful, morbid ordeal. We need to understand that human beings also have mental and spiritual bodies that are integrated with the physical. Viewing humans merely as physical beings is fundamentally flawed because it separates us from our essential wholeness. The physical aspect of being cannot be dissociated from mental and spiritual ones. Both illness and wellness at any level are connected to all other levels of being.

Nevertheless, we don't hear cancer being described as hopeful, loving, healing, balancing, transformative, or spiritual, even though it often creates profound, positive changes in the ways we relate to ourselves and others. Now, I'm not saying that cancer is a "gift", but it can bring out the best in people even as they experience tremendous pain. As we move away from self-blame, fear, anger, guilt, and worry toward self-love, acceptance, surrender, insight, and love, we connect to more than just the body and the mind. We connect to the spiritual qualities that arise due to the existential issues that accompany cancer. Then, a more integrated, whole-being response may come forward. Cancer also has the potential to transform those around us. Our relationships with our closest loved ones may expand to a fuller love heretofore unexperienced, while support from our community lessens the ego, revealing the underlying unity in the apparent diversity of beings.

For me, I saw cancer as a metaphor for an imbalance in the flow of energy in the first three sheaths of the self—food/physical, energy/energetic, and mind/mental sheaths. (See Appendix E.) This imbalance centered in the reproductive area of the physical body and corresponded to the energetic centers of the reproductive organs, which further connected to the mind. After all, what is cancer? It is a metabolic disease where cells behave abnormally to survive. Cells can die from getting too much or too little energy. Too much energy leads to inhibition of respiration, and too little energy leads to cellular death or necrosis.[8] Such imbalance in the flow of energy is the basis of all disease. Proper cellular functioning occurs when cells maintain homeostasis, which is why touching into Wholeness is healing. It helps to reset the flow of energy.

Whole New Me

Although this book is about my experience with cancer,

my spiritual journey started decades before I was diagnosed. Ever since I was a child, I wanted to be free, and this desire motivated me to explore my psyche through the years. This longing for liberation, though unconscious in the beginning, led me to take step after step in my spiritual journey. I was blessed to have found a spiritual teacher in this life who knew how to help me. As spiritual life was progressing, enormous challenges like cancer also manifested, so life could be both good and dreadful. Regardless of these vicissitudes, it was spiritual awareness that helped me to observe these dramas without getting swept away by them. It was spiritual awareness that facilitated both a disidentification with individual ego and the experience of merging into the One. Uncovering the spiritual essence of being is truly what healed my body, mind, and soul. I was lacking creative expression and needed to bring joy into every level of being to facilitate the unfolding of a Whole new me. In every crisis, there is opportunity. As I reflect on the meaning of cancer in my life, it has been one of integrating body, mind, and spirit as an expression of Wholeness, Consciousness, or Oneness.

Appendix A: The Manifestation Process and the Evolution of Mind

In order to understand my mental conditioning and how it contributed to the development of my cancer, I need to explain 1) what the mind is within the schema of the Samkhya (pronounced san-kiah) process of creation, and 2) the modes of the mind (explained in Appendix B). It may seem unnecessary to define the mind because it is such an ordinary part of our daily experiences, but most of us never think about what the mind really is or how it works. If pressed to define the mind, it would be hard to conceptualize. An apt metaphor for understanding the mind is driving a car. Driving is a common daily experience, but few understand how a car actually works. In order to explain the mind and the mental conditioning that contributed to the development of my cancer, I need to first present the "process of creation" (or classification of phenomena) based on Samkhya philosophy that is the basis of many Indian philosophies. Samkhya is the theoretical counterpart to yoga, an applied philosophy. People may not realize that the yoga practiced in studios actually has theoretical roots in Samkhya. Yoga is a comprehensive system for transforming the individual self into the universal Self in an experiential manner just as Samkhya explains how the individual evolves out of universal, unmanifest Matter in a theoretical way. I ask the reader to bear with me through this abstruse philosophical part, but it was fundamental to my understanding of the mind's role in what happened to me. I don't present Samkhya to proselytize but to provide a conceptual scaffold to better comprehend the mental and spiritual sections of this book. Additionally, the process of creation according to Samkhya is presented briefly for the purpose of sharing my story. Readers who want to learn more may consult other sources.[1,2]

The Process of Manifestation in Samkhya

The founding sage of Samkhya was Kapila (circa 6th century BCE).[3] A dualistic philosophy, Samkhya purports that there are two unchanging, eternal, and coexisting realities: Purusha and Prakriti. Purusha is the eternal Observer or Witness that is Consciousness itself, and Prakriti is the eternal source of Unmanifest Matter. Purusha (Consciousness) is beyond any attributes and cannot be defined or limited. It is beyond the mind, thoughts, and words. It exists eternally as Consciousness itself. Think of the "observer within" instead of the actor or doer. For example, when you are dreaming, you are acting in the dream as yourself, but who is observing the dream? That is the Observer. On account of what is called "the light of Consciousness (Observer)," the mind is aware of the dream. The mind uses the light of Consciousness to function, but it does not have its own light. We mistakenly equate mind and Consciousness because we use the mind to perceive or know phenomena, but the mind is merely an instrument of Consciousness and not Consciousness itself. It is like thinking that a reel of film projected onto a movie screen is what allows us to perceive the movie when it is really the light within the projector instead of the film. The film is akin to the contents of the mind (memories), and the mind is like the projector (merely an instrument), but it is due to the light (Consciousness) that we see the movie.

Prakriti is eternal Unmanifest Matter that is in a state of equilibrium—a balance of the three gunas or modes of matter called sattva (qualities of light, sentience, purity), rajas (qualities of activity, movement, passion), and tamas (qualities of inertia, inactivity, dullness). When Purusha (Consciousness) and Prakriti (Unmanifest Matter) come into contact, Prakriti's equilibrium becomes disturbed, and creation begins (matter begins to manifest). Creation occurs when the three gunas of light, action, and inertia are stimulated. When the light of Consciousness penetrates the unconscious darkness of Matter, the universe—and everything within it—is born. All manifested matter is an evolute of (comes from) Prakriti, but it is Purusha's seed (Consciousness) that "impregnates" Prakriti. She, in turn, births all of creation through the changing ratio of the three gunas (disruption of the equilibrium of equal ratios or balance).

Figure 2 illustrates the 23 evolutes of Consciousness in Samkhya.[4] When Purusha interacts with Prakruti, the

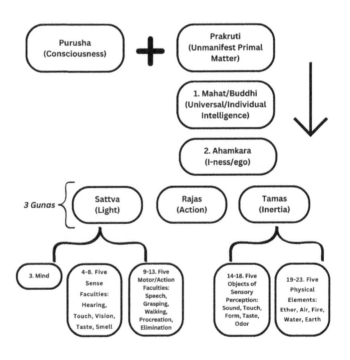

Figure 2. Samkhya Process of Manifestation

sentience of Consciousness initiates Prakruti (Unmanifest Potential) and manifestation ensues. It is this Creative Power, Prakruti, that stirs the entire universe from the subtlest expression of energy to the densest. Consider an unstruck drum that makes no sound (passive or unmanifest) versus the first strike (active or manifest) that produces sound. Another example is to consider a serene pond that is completely still. When you drop a stone into the pond, ripples appear. The stillness is the passive, latent pond, and the ripples are the active, manifest pond. In Samkhya, this is what all phenomena or manifest matter (from spiritual to mental to physical) is: the transformation of matter into other forms that appear as diversities through the changing ratio of the qualities of light, action, and inertia (the gunas). In Samkhya, matter cannot be ultimately destroyed as Prakriti is eternal; it just transforms into another form (via new combinations of the gunas). Consider the example of a burnt piece of wood. The wood is gone but not completely destroyed; it turned into ash. This also occurs at more subtle levels of manifestation. When we experience something happy, sad, or fearful and then later we don't remember it, the feeling appears to be gone, but it is actually stored at an unconscious level of the mind. From the standpoint of the gunas, here is what happens. Tamas guna, which has the qualities of inertia and dullness, predominates, but sattva guna, which has the quality of light and sentience, and rajas guna, which has the qualities of action and movement, become less active. That is why it is hard to remember something at the unconscious level. When tamas guna predominates, it is hard to be aware, perceptive, and active (qualities of sattva and rajas).

The First and Second Evolutes of Matter

Mahad is the initial manifestation (the first evolute) of matter. It is the first expression of creation, like the Word or Logos in Christian traditions. This is Intelligence at the universal level, a level of higher order functions such as intuition. Mahad is universal intelligence which has not yet differentiated into an individual level. When it does, it is known as Buddhi, the individual intellect responsible for discrimination, intelligence, judgment. Here's an example to help clarify the meaning. When energy is focused, it creates a center which moves that energy from an undifferentiated to a differentiated form. Think of light, which shines down from the sun as diffuse and omnipresent at the universal level. When that same light is focused into a laser, it "appears" as a point of light in bounded form at the individual level. Appearance is really just transformation of energy.[5]

After the principle of individual intelligence is born, Ahamkara or "I"ness, the second evolute, is created. To continue with the example from before, after the individual intellect is focused as a specific center or point, identification with that point as "I" begins. It is through this I-making function (ego) that identification with accumulated thoughts (memories) occurs; it makes us identify with memories as ours. The stronger these identifications are (through reinforcement), the greater the ego's attachment to them. It is this I-making function that personalizes all the objective workings of the mind and intellect. With repetition, we start to believe we are our individual thoughts and memories. This I-ness is also overlaid onto the body so that we think that where the physical body ends so do we. We forget that we are unlimited, pure Consciousness which is far more extensive than the physical body or the mind.

The Three Gunas: Sattva, Rajas, and Tamas

The three universal qualities called gunas exist in all phenomena.[6] They are not considered as separate evolutes because they are inherent in all evolutes of Prakriti since all manifest matter is comprised of differing ratios of their combinations. When Prakriti is unmanifest, these three gunas are latent and in equilibrium, but as creation unfolds, they become potent (active) and manifest into all phenomena, from universal to individual levels. Every "object" in the universe, whether subtle like a thought or physical like a stone, is a combination of these three qualities in differing ratios. All of phenomena—all manifestations—whether subtle or material, are objects in relation to Consciousness. Consciousness is the Observer that witnesses the display of Prakriti's manifesting actions. As noted earlier, at the universal level, sattva guna is the essence of pure perception (light), rajas guna is movement or action, and tamas guna is inertia or darkness. After the I-making function (ego) is created at the individual level, sattva becomes the knower (perception), rajas becomes the process of knowing (perceiving, which is active behavior), and tamas becomes the known object (the perceived, which is an inert object).

The Evolutes of Sattva Guna: The Mind Evolves from Sattva Guna

From sattva guna (the quality of perception or light), three main faculties are created: the mind (faculty of cognition/action), the sense faculties (hearing, touch, vision, taste, and smell), and motor faculties (speech, grasping, walking, procreation, elimination). All of these faculties facilitate perception, awareness, and knowing. That is why they fall under sattva guna—the "quality of light"—because light helps us to see, perceive, and have vision.

When sattva guna and rajas guna interact, the sattvic faculties of mind, sensory and motor perception are stimulated into action. Now we get to an understanding of what the mind is and how it evolves from the interaction of Consciousness and Unmanifest or Primal Matter. Mind is an instrument (faculty) that allows perception (knowing) to occur as we interact with our external and internal environments. It is comprised of cognitive, sensory, and motor faculties along with memory and ego. The sense faculties, known as *jnanendriyas*, include hearing, touch, vision, taste, and smell. They are not material objects like a table which has a gross form and can be perceived by physical sense organs. Vision is not a material object; it is a subtle sense faculty.

The interaction of sattvic and rajasic qualities (perception plus action qualities) also initiates action faculties, *karmendriyas*, that include speech, grasping (with arms/hands), walking, procreation, and elimination. These faculties are also subtle although they seem physical. We know (perceive) the subtle faculty of walking by using the physical legs, so we may think that the motor faculty of walking exists at the gross material level. But the motor faculty is experienced at a more subtle level than physical movement; it is also experienced at the level of mind. Think of the difference between walking in waking life versus in a dream. Although the body is paralyzed while dreaming, you still perceive that you are walking, even though the "action" of walking is a subtle (mental)—not physical—faculty.

The Evolutes of Tamas Guna

From tamas guna (the quality of inertia or darkness), the tanmatras—or objects of sensory perception (sound, touch, form, taste, and odor)—and the five mahabhutas—or physical elements (ether, air, fire, water, earth)—are created. The tanmatras are the subtle forms or subtle objects of the physical elements. Subtle elements precede physical ones in evolution. Tamas guna has a more dull, unconscious quality, but this inertia (lack of awareness) should not be confused with the ultimate stillness of Consciousness, which is Supreme Awareness. Whereas the sattvic sensory faculties of hearing, touching, sight, taste, and smell allow perception to occur, the tamasic objects of perception (sound, touch, form, taste, and odor) are what is experienced. They are subtle, not physical, objects. But when phenomena become even more tamasic (the ratio of the gunas favors tamas), then the physical elements are created. When tamas guna interacts with rajas guna, a mixed quality of inertia and action is created. At the grossest level of creation, this mixture of energy manifests as the physical elements. Ether (space), air, fire, water, and earth are physical elements, and we perceive them at the physical level of awareness with our physical senses.

The process of creation from the interaction of Consciousness with Matter is one of increasing differentiation or diversity. I present it here briefly to provide a deeper understanding of my healing journey back to Consciousness from physical matter—from the fragmented me to the Wholeness (the differentiated to the Undifferentiated). It is the Wholeness that heals us from physical and mental imbalances. We are already Whole, but we identify with being less than whole, which allows illness or imbalance to take hold over time. There is an essential integrity in Wholeness that, when disturbed, creates the hall of mirrors of worldly phenomena. Imbalance occurs as we identify with these reflections over time instead of identifying with the Wholeness. Greater integration of our whole being taps into healing, creative, spiritual energy which has unlimited potential and can even result in radical, seemingly spontaneous healing.[7,8]

Appendix B: Modes of the Mind

In yoga philosophy, the mind modulates through five main modes: correct perception, incorrect perception (misperception), imagination/fantasy, sleep, and memory.[1]

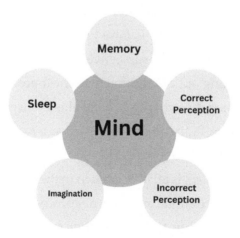

Figure 3: Modes of the Mind

Figure 3 illustrates these modes. The first mode, correct perception (*pramana*—cognition of something), occurs through perception, inference, and testimony. We perceive through our sensory organs as we interact with our environments. Although there are limits to the physical senses in that humans can only hear within a specific range of frequencies or see a certain distance, we generally acquire knowledge through our physical senses. We also make inferences (conclusions reached through evidence and reason) to gather knowledge. For example, when dark clouds appear, we infer that it will rain. We can also know something through another's testimony, such as when a friend tells you what a specific neighborhood in Paris is like even though you have never been there.

The second mode, incorrect perception (*viparyaya*—misperception or illusion), is false knowledge that appears to be true based on our subjective perception of it. For example, thinking out of fear that a medical procedure will be harmful when it's actually beneficial is a misperception. Perceiving a dark figure in the back yard as a monster when it's actually a tree is another. The third mode, fantasy or imagination (*vikalpa*), is an idea created in the mind that isn't true. This is a more subtle and internal process than the first two modes of mind in that it does not require perception through the physical senses. It is a mental projection, a daydream. Imagining what it would be like to climb Mt.

Everest is an example of imagination. The fourth mode is sleep (*nidra*), which occurs when the mind has no mental content. Sleep occurs when the mind is not in the other modes. The fifth mode, memory (*smriti*), occurs when the mind recollects a prior experience.

As we interact with outer and inner environments, the mind is constantly perceiving, inferring, misunderstanding, projecting, daydreaming, fantasizing, and remembering. At times, the mind is more focused externally with taking in information through the senses. At other times, it is focused more internally with thinking about that information. During still other periods, the mind is imagining thoughts, remembering them, or sleeping. The mind is constantly cycling through these modes. When the mind stops modifying (moving from mode to mode) altogether, undifferentiated (pure) Consciousness is what remains.

Meditation, not sleep, is the means through which we learn to stop our mental modifications. The mind may have temporarily stopped its activity in sleep, but this doesn't mean it has stopped modifying in any permanent sense. The mind gets an opportunity to rest, but it will continue to modulate when we wake up. For example, we may sleep every night, but when we wake up, we are no more aware than before. Through sleep, we return to unconsciousness where tamas guna prevails at the individual level, but it is not the same as transcending all phenomena and realizing

Consciousness (liberation).

When we meditate, however, we learn how to stop our mental modifications, and gradually, awareness expands. When mental modifications stop, the mind becomes aligned with Consciousness. The more established we become in stopping mental modifications and thereby resting in Consciousness itself, the more we bring Consciousness through the mind and its modifications. As long as we live, the mind will modify even if we are liberated. But when we are established in Consciousness, the mind becomes more of a pure instrument of perception rather than an instrument filtered through the matrix of individual conditions or personality. You experience a universal mind rather than an individual or personal mind. Intuition occurs at this level of Mahat (universal intellect) versus Buddhi (individual intellect). See Appendix D for further discussion of intuition.

Appendix C: Karma

Mental patterns are born from actions, both good and bad, called karma in Indian philosophies. Karma is popularly described as "what goes around comes around," but it is more precisely defined in Indian philosophy as the totality of our thoughts, words, and deeds and their consequences.[1] When an individual has thoughts, utters words, or performs actions, latent impressions are created and produce results. Every human life is a process of making choices and taking actions. It is these decisions that constitute karma—the principle of cause and effect or action and reaction. Karma refers not only to past deeds but also present ones and is responsible for the entire sequence of cause and effect. In this way, karma binds souls to the world based on their actions, so it functions as a moral doctrine, akin to "we reap what we sow." Karma is also not the same thing as fate because fate is a predestined outcome beyond an individual's control. The central pillar in karma is freedom of will (freedom of choice), not fatalism. An individual is constantly altering their karma moment by moment depending on their mental, verbal, and behavioral choices. We create our own lives, and our choices direct how our lives unfold. Individuals, not some deity or divinity, are responsible for their lives.

There are four types of karma: *sanchita karma*, which is the totality of all our karma accumulated over all lifetimes; *parabdha karma*, which is the present life's portion of karma that is ripe enough to produce consequences currently; *agami karma*, the portion of karma from the current lifetime's actions to be added to the totality of karma (sanchita); and *kriyamana karma*, which is being created in the current lifetime (immediate karma).[2] An example of kriyamana karma is when you get a ticket for speeding. You perform the action (speeding) and immediately reap the consequences of that action (ticket). Similarly, when you think negative thoughts about winning a game and wind up losing, that is another example of immediate karma. My personal example of parabdha karma (ripened karma) is having ovarian cancer surgery. I had accumulated memories of painful female castration procedures plus the loss of traditional women's roles during previous lifetimes, and these memories, combined with my present actions, had ripened enough to produce fruit in this life. So, I wasn't fated to have ovarian cancer and reexperience surgery on reproductive organs, rather my mind held deep attachments to the trauma from those past experiences, and these karmas had ripened enough to produce fruit under the right conditions—pattern of cancer in the family, stress, unhealthy diet, deterioration of the physical terrain, and lack of interest in the material world—in the present life.

When we perform karma without attachment or without expectation of outcomes, we simply perform the deed without egoic passion. We are performing actions purely as the Observer rather than by the invested self (ego). These types of actions don't produce karma. This is one of the profound teachings in the Bhagavad Gita, a Hindu scripture written by Veda Vyasa. When we perform actions with attachment or ego, however, the degree of attachment will determine the degree of intensity we experience when the consequences of that karma ripen in present or future lives.[3] Similarly, work or actions that we perform for others without ego and not for ourselves also don't produce karma.

According to the Yoga Sutras of Patanjali, there are three main consequences of one's actions: birth, lifespan, and the experience of pleasure and pain.[4] Depending on an individual's actions over a lifetime, a person may be born into various birth forms such as a celestial being, human, animal, insect, vegetable, or mineral. For example, if a person mostly acted beastly in this lifetime even though born a human, the mind would store these actions and their associated feelings of pleasure and pain. After death and at the time of the next birth, these latent tendencies may produce a birth into an animal body instead of a human one. Humans and animals are similar except humans have self-awareness, although some people act no better than animals even though they are human. If an individual did not wisely use the precious human gift of self-awareness, then rebirth into an animal form is possible as a consequence of prior actions and attachment to thoughts and behaviors. The length of a person's life also depends on an individual's actions, as do the pleasure and pain they experience in the current life. These latent impressions of actions are called *karmasaya*.

Feelings associated with the three consequences of actions are called vasanas. For example, I had latent impressions of having undergone surgery from my priestess life (karmasaya) and subliminal emotions of fear (vasanas) associated with those actions. Latent (dormant) impressions are subconscious or below the threshold of conscious awareness, yet they still influence the mind. When conditions are right, they become potent (active or ripe). In any lifetime, impressions are stored both from actions and feelings associated with those actions. Through concentration and meditation, I became aware of my karma and how prior actions from previous lifetimes had consequences in my current life. However, as previously explained, karma is not fatalistic. Just because you did something before, you are not karmically destined for the same fate later. You always have free will to choose your thoughts, words, and actions at any moment, which adds to and changes your karma dynamically. An individual is not a programmed robot. Karma is the storehouse of prior actions, their consequences, and associated feelings as well as our mental conditioning or patterns of thinking, feeling, and acting. You are always free to overwrite negative patterns with positive ones.

Appendix D: Intuition

Intuition is defined as knowing something immediately without using reason or inference.[1] For example, if we see smoke, we can infer that a fire has occurred because smoke is associated with fire. However, if we intuit that a fire will occur even when there are no signs of one, that perception may be called intuition if in fact a fire does occur. I had an intellectual understanding of intuition as knowing something without using logical conclusions, but I didn't really know what it truly was until my spiritual life developed and it occurred more often. That is when I realized there is a difference between intuition, intuitive perception, and gut feelings or hunches, though their effects may be similar. I want to explain the differences between these different types of knowing because intuition played a key role in my healing process. Not enough credit goes to the spiritual aspect of healing because it is a subtle, inner process that is not well understood, defined, and studied. It is also difficult to observe and relies upon personal testimony. Nonetheless, for me, it was the most significant part of navigating cancer and healing from it.

Intuition is "inner tuition" that comes from a highly concentrated mind. It is still experienced by the mind but by one that is on the verge of absorption (being transcended) in contrast to a modulating, unfocused mind. That is why intuition is more of a spiritual experience than a mental one even though it occurs through the mind. At the same time, intuition cannot be experienced when the mind is absorbed into Consciousness because there is no instrument to report the experience. When the mind no longer modulates, you rest in Consciousness alone. Nothing else exists, not even the mind (hence "the self" also disappears). Awareness alone exists. This Oneness experience has been described using many analogies such as going to another shore (transcending mind), stopping the world, abiding in the gap, melting into the ocean, going back home, or removing the layers of Self. When the mind is absorbed back into Consciousness, there is no phenomena, but when you return (reorientation) from absorption, mind reappears and modulation restarts (reappearance of phenomena including the ego/self).

Appendix D

The type of intuition I'm describing is a subtle and refined "pre-absorption" experience that occurs in a mind that has become more of a pure instrument than one of conditioned responses filled with the seeds of personality or individual ego. As the absorption experience becomes more established, the ego thins out, and though some ego remains, it is not greatly conditioned by personality. Traversing the road from concentrated mind toward absorption, the traveler becomes well acquainted with intuition: a knowing that occurs in a still mind prior to the re-activation of mental modification. When you return from absorption, the mind initially moves slowly and has not yet gained traction. When the mind first reappears, this inner tuition may be inwardly heard or "known without hearing." Intuition may also be experienced as a perceptive knowing or gut feeling in certain modes if the mind is concentrated.

We experience intuitive knowing through degrees of concentration as the mind cycles through its modes. The more focused the mind is as it modulates, the fewer external/internal perceptions come in, which facilitates concentration. When the mind cycles through its modes, the Observer is obscured, but when the mind stops modulating, the Observer alone exists (shines through resplendently). Intuition also occurs when the mind is concentrated during one of its modes. For example, if the mind is in correct perception mode and the degree of concentration is high, thereby reducing external and internal noise, intuitive perception can occur. We are intuitive beings because we are already Whole (One), but constant mental fluctuations can obscure this inherent and natural ability within us.

Neuroscience and Intuition

To further explain what intuition is, turning to neuroscience may be helpful. Consider the brain's evolutionary development over millions of years. As each developmental addition emerged, different functions arose, influencing the development of our species. In the 1960s, neuroscientist and physician Paul MacLean developed his triune model of the brain that included the reptilian, limbic, and neocortex complexes.[2] Broadly put, the reptilian brain or R-complex was responsible for physical survival (automatic/involuntary physiological functions), the limbic controlled emotions (most memory), and the neocortex directed thinking (intellect, processing sensory information, voluntary movement). Neuroscience and related disciplines have developed extensively since then and moved away from areas of the brain to complex and dynamic networks of the brain.[3,4] One of the main networks is the default mode network (DMN) which is comprised of three major subdivisions: the ventral prefrontal cortex (VMPC), the dorsal medial prefrontal cortex (DMPC), and the posterior cingulate cortex (PCC).[5] The VMPC receives sensory information that it conveys to the emotional processing centers of the brain, so when an individual perceives that information, there is an emotional evaluation which then influences behavior. The DMPC functions during self-referential activity when individuals think about themselves. The PCC is active when recollecting something (memory).

Though the dominant view in neuroscience is that consciousness and the mind are the same, yoga philosophy proposes that they are distinct, which aligns with my experience. It is difficult to study refined, subtle, inner states within the parameters of objective research studies, so neurologists study brain activity while research participants execute an inner task such as visualizing something or meditating. To my knowledge, there have not been any studies while participants are in absorption. There would be significant recruitment challenges for a study of this type, further complicated by the fact that there are degrees of meditation prior to absorption. Limitations aside, neuroscientists Vaibhav Tripathi and Pallavi Bharadwaj have proposed a yogic theory of consciousness model to explain brain network activity as the mind modulates or is transcended.[6] They propose that default mode and attention networks in the brain may be abstracted to represent the mind with the prefrontal cortex as the intellect, the medial frontal cortex as the ego (self-referencing), and the hippocampus and amygdala regions as memory. As the mind modulates, different brain networks and regions may be co-active, and connectivity to Consciousness (the Seer) is reduced. For example, when the mind is in memory mode, memory regions are activated and the attention network that would take in sensory data is disregarded. When the mind is taking in sensory and motor data such as walking in a park, all of the attention networks are attended to by the brain. During deep dreamless sleep, however, all the networks of the brain are disregarded, and the same for absorption, as the mind is completely transcended, and Consciousness alone exists.

Gut Feelings, Intuition, and Emotions

Now, consider the experience of having a gut feeling, gut instinct, or hunch. It is similar to an intuition in that we "know" something is right or it will work even if we haven't arrived there by logic. At the physiological level, the gastrointestinal tract is controlled by the enteric nervous system (ENS) which is a part of the peripheral nervous system (the nervous system outside the brain and spinal cord). The ENS determines movement patterns in the gastrointestinal tract, controls acid secretion, changes blood flow, modifies nutrient handling, and interacts with the immune and endocrine systems of the gut.[7] Since the discovery of the ENS, along with advances in neuroscience and microbiology, we now know that gut-brain crosstalk is bidirectional, not only ensuring proper digestive health but also affecting cognitive functions like intuitive decision making.[8] This is why the ENS is often called "the second brain." Gut sensations like stomach pain, nausea, hunger, and satiety are connected to interoceptive (awareness of inner sensations) memories of feeling pleasure and pain.[9,10] These associated feelings arising from memory not only steer us away from eating spoiled food, but they also help us make decisions based upon our gut. Gut intuitions may thus be a rapid processing of probable risks or rewards based upon our memories.[11]

In addition to discussing gut feelings or hunches, explaining the difference between feelings and emotions may be helpful for understanding intuition. Feelings are conscious experiences that we are aware of such as "I feel happy, sad, or anxious." Emotions, however, are subconscious experiences (deep memory) that we are not fully aware of at the conscious level.[12] Feelings and emotions are used interchangeably in common speech, but they are experienced with different degrees of awareness. For example, I had a deep emotion (mental conditioning) of grief over losing a child in my memory from a previous incarnation, but it was expressed as a feeling of sadness about family life at the conscious level in the present. I was aware of feeling sadness about family life, but I was unaware of the deeper emotion of grief of losing that child.

When I became conscious of this past-life pattern, it was no longer hidden. Through awareness, I was able to observe it, contemplate it, and choose to think and behave differently.

Intuition vs. Insight

Intuition has been classified broadly as intuitive knowledge or intuitive insight because there is still much to know about the mind's cognitive structure.[13] Insight comes from waking and dreaming states that are limited by their respective faculties of perception. For example, when we try to solve problems, the mind works on it with reason (waking state), imagination (daydreams), and memories or feelings (dreams). Often, an insight will come in a dream or in a non-attentive state such as daydreaming when the reasoning mind has stopped thinking about it. Mental concentration (motivated by desire) sets the conditions for an insight to emerge whether in the waking, daydreaming, or dreaming state. The question or problem concentrates the mind from its normal unfocused tendency which allows otherwise unnoticed knowledge to appear.

Intuition, however, comes from a less active but more focused mind than that experienced in waking, daydreaming, and dreaming states. It may help us to solve problems or answer questions as insight does but comes from a different level of concentrated mind. My experience of intuition is that it is an immediate, holistic, inner

Appendix D

experience facilitated by subtle cognitive faculties at the level of the mind. Recall that the mind consists of individual intellect (buddhi), I-ness (ego), subtle sensory and motor faculties, and memory. Intuition is a sattvic (characterized by light or sentience) experience of the mind and not one with great amounts of rajas (characterized by activity) or tamas gunas (characterized by inertia). Intuition is an experience of pure knowing or knowing unadulterated by ego and memory. It is a sattvic manifestation of Awareness or Consciousness. It is an experience of Mahat—universal intellect. This is why intuition is immediately trusted despite human bias towards reason. It is similar to how we are more likely to trust someone's opinion who doesn't have an agenda or ego involved in a problem we are trying to solve than someone who has a vested interest. Intuition also provides an immediate sense of confidence because it is closer to Wholeness, our essence, than our individual, egoic experience which is varied and fragmented. It comes from a more whole place even though we experience it through an individual ego.

In my experience, intuition can be helpful as advance notification of phenomena that has not yet manifested at the physical level. Intuition appears to have a precognitive effect because in the waking state (physical reality), time is a factor (i.e., time exists). During the dream state (mental reality), memory is time. At the spiritual level (beyond

163

mind), however, time doesn't exist. There is simply existence itself (Consciousness). The perception of time, just like the perception of color, is a mental object from the viewpoint of Consciousness and not absolutely real. Time and color aren't permanent. There is only Consciousness itself, always existing regardless of an individual being absorbed or in a mode of the mind.

Appendix E: Five Sheaths of Human Existence

Previously, I explained the process of creation based on the dualistic philosophy of Samkhya. Now, I present another way to understand the descent of Spirit into matter based on the Upanishads—Vedic philosophical scriptures dealing with existential topics such as the nature of reality, self, and Consciousness, that inform Vedanta, another Indian philosophical school that is monistic. Vedanta has been said to be the logical outcome of Samkhya as dualism ultimately turns into monism (Oneness).[1]

As explained in the Taittiriya Upanishad, there are five sheaths (*pancha koshas*) of human existence.[2] These sheaths, as illustrated in Figure 4, comprise the entire spectrum of being human, from the most gross physical level to the most spiritual, transcendent level of existence. They are commonly

WHOLE NEW ME

referred to as "bodies" for ease of understanding, as in food body, energy body, mental body, intellect body, and bliss or causal (seed) body. Think of Russian matryoshka nesting dolls as a visual example of these sheaths of existence.

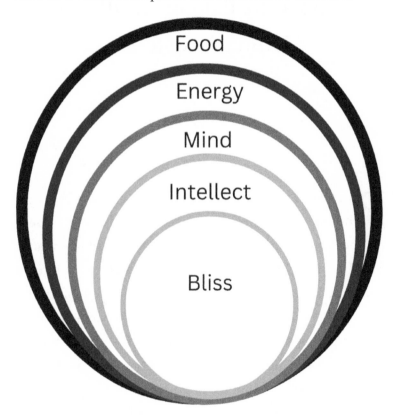

Figure 4: Five Sheaths of Human Existence

The first (outer) sheath is the food sheath (*Annamaya kosha*), comprised of the physical body. It is the physical aspect of human personality. This sheath includes our entire

166

physical being (plasma, blood, muscle, fat, bone, marrow, and reproductive tissue) and is nourished by the food we eat. The second sheath is the energy body (*Pranamaya kosha*). It surrounds and influences the physical body but is more subtle. It is a network of non-physical energy channels that may be understood as the aura. It is the underlying energy field of the physical body, and vital life force (prana) moves through it. Think of the human form as having an energetic replica to imagine this sheath. The third sheath is the mental body (*Manomaya kosha*) or mind. This is the vehicle for our thoughts and is more subtle than the prior two. We cannot perceive thoughts through the physical body because they are subtle, but we can feel the effects of thoughts on our physical body because the sheaths are all interconnected. For example, if we have a fearful thought, it directly affects how energy flows in our energy sheath, which then influences the physical body (changes in breathing, release of hormones, and stimulation of nervous system). The fourth body is the intellect sheath (*Vijnanamaya kosha*)—the vehicle of discrimination and judgment that can determine right from wrong. It is the arena of determinative knowing free from the doubtful thinking that is experienced in the mental sheath. The fifth body is the bliss sheath (*Anandamaya kosha*) where joy and creativity emanate.

Each of these sheaths is progressively more subtle and

expansive and represented here as larger circles being less expansive and smaller circles being more expansive. At the grossest level, the physical body is bound by the size of the body, but at the level of the bliss body, bliss can ripple through all the sheaths (the entire universe). That is why bliss experienced at the causal body level (causal, seed, and bliss body are interchangeable terms) is so profound; it's an experience far greater than mere happiness or feeling joyful at an egoic level. The bliss experienced at this sheath is not to be confused with the feeling of individual happiness or personal passion. Instead, it is an intoxicating, unifying feeling that throbs from the universal level to the individual human experience. An individual who has transcended the ego (individual level of being) will be able to experience this universal bliss.

These five sheaths may be thought of as a human being's "personality" (descent of Spirit into matter).[3] Each one serves as an energetic vehicle (body) through which Consciousness is experienced, albeit in limited ways compared to the unlimited awareness of Consciousness. The light of Pure Consciousness is obscured by the qualities of each sheath, so humans must evolve beyond the limits of the sheaths to know Unlimited Consciousness, which could be represented as a dot in the center of the Bliss circle in Figure 4. I share this Upanishadic/Vedantic model of the five sheaths to further explain how I needed to fully integrate the light of Pure Consciousness all the way down to the physical level as part of my healing. Ironically, the experience of cancer brought Spirit all the way down to my physical body. It wasn't enough to experience absorption alone; I had to bring this awareness back into my world in an integrated manner, which took some time and required adjustment to a different way of being.

Notes

INTRODUCTION

1. "heal (v.)," Online Etymology Dictionary. https://www. etymonline.com/word/heal. Accessed December 27, 2021.
2. Hariharānanda Arānya S. *Yoga Philosophy of Patanjali.* SUNY; 1983.
3. Sivananda S. *The Bhagavad Gita.* Divine Life Trust Society; 2010.
4. Venkatesananda S. *Vasistha's Yoga.* SUNY; 1993.
5. Niranjanananda S. *Samkhya Darhsan/Yogic Perspective on Theories of Realism.* Yoga Publications Trust; 2008.

CHAPTER 1: THE BODY

1. Frisco SW, Choi SW. The potential cocarcinogenic effect of vitamin B12 deficiency," *Clin Chem Lab Med.* 2005; 43(10):1158-1163. doi:10.1515/CCLM.2005.201
2. Lacombe V, Chabrun F, Lacout C, et al. Persistent elevation of plasma vitamin B12 is strongly associated with solid cancer," *Sci Rep.* 2021;11(13361):1-7. doi:10.1038/s41598-021-92945-y

3. Holick MF, Chen TC. Vitamin D deficiency: A worldwide problem with health consequences. *Am J Clin Nutr.* 2008;87(4):1080S-1086S. doi:10.1093/ajcn/87.4.1080S

4. Stomach cancer statistics. World Cancer Research Fund International. https://www.wcrf.org/dietandcancer/stomach-cancer-statistics/. Accessed January 15, 2022.

5. Abadi ATB, Ierardi E, Lee Y. Why do we still have helicobacter pylori in our stomachs." *Malays J Med Sci.* 2015;22(5):70-75.

6. Helicobacter pylori and cancer. National Cancer Institute. https://www.cancer.gov/about-cancer/causes-prevention/risk/infectious-agents/h-pylori-fact-sheet.Accessed December 27, 2021.

7. Bristol stool chart. Continence Foundation of Australia. https://www.continence.org.au/bristol-stool-chart. Accessed on January 15, 2022.

8. Wankhade SS, Thorwat VK. Scientific significance of abhyanga (massage)," *Dheerghayu International.* 2017;33(129):31-35.

9. Lad V and Durve A. *Marma Points of Ayurveda.* The Ayurvedic Press; 2008.

10. Suprapubic catheter. Bladder & Bowel Community. https://www.bladderandbowel.org/surgical-treatment/suprapubic-catheter/. Accessed January 15, 2022.

11. Endovascular coiling for brain aneurysms. Johns Hopkins Medicine. https://www.hopkinsmedicine.org/neurology_neurosurgery/centers_clinics/aneurysm/treatment/aneurysm_endovascular_coiling.html. Accessed January 15, 2022.

12. Friedman M. The human stress response. In: Bernady N, Friedman M. eds. *A Practical Guide to PTSD Treatment: Pharmacological and Psychotherapeutic Approaches.* American Psychological Association; 2015:9-19.

13. Stress effects on the body. American Psychological Association. https://www.apa.org/topics/stress/body. Accessed January 9, 2022.

14. Tsigos C, Kyrou I, Kassi E, et al. Stress: Endocrine physiology and pathophysiology. In: eds. Feingold K, Anawalt B, Boyce A, et al. *Endotext.* MDText.com, Inc; 2000, updated 2020.

15. Yarigebi H, Panahi Y, Hedayat S, et al. The impact of stress on body function: A review. *EXCLI J.* 2017;16:1057-1072. doi:10.17179/excli2017-480

16. Thaker PH, Lutgendorf SK, Sood SK. The neuroendocrine impact of chronic stress on cancer. *Cell Cycle.* 2007;6(4):430-433. doi:10.4161/ cc.6.4.3829

17. Winters N, Kelley J. *The Metabolic Approach to Cancer: Integrating Deep Nutrition, the Ketogenic Diet, and Nontoxic Bio-Individualized Therapies.* Chelsea Green; 2017:3-5.

18. CDC museum COVID-19 timeline. Centers for Disease Control and Prevention. https://www.cdc.gov/museum/timeline/covid19.html. Accessed January 10, 2022.

19. Jahanafrooz Z, Baradaran B, Mosafer J, et al. Comparison of DNA and mRNA vaccines against cancer. *Drug Discov.* 2021; 25(3):552–560. doi: 10.1016/j.drudis.2019.12.003

20. Bhatti SI, Mindikoglu AL. The impact of dawn to sunset fasting on immune system and its clinical significance in COVID-19 pandemic. *Metabolism Open.* 2022;13(100162). doi: 10.1016/j.metop.2021.100162

21. Rapp K, Schroeder J, Klenk J, et al. Fasting blood glucose and cancer risk in a cohort of more than 140,000 adults in Australia. *Diabetologia*. 2006;49: 945-952. doi:10.1007/s00125-006-0207-6

22. Seyfried TN, Mukherjee P, Targeting energy metabolism in brain cancer: Review and hypothesis. *Nutr Metab*. 2005;2:30. doi:10.1186/1743-7075-2-30

23. Schmidt MI, Hadji-Georgopoulos A, Rendell M, et al. The dawn phenomenon, an early morning glucose rise: Implications for diabetic intraday blood glucose variation. *Diabetes Care*. 1981;4(6):579-585.

24. Mean fasting blood glucose. World Health Organization, https://www.who.int/data/gho/indicator-metadata-registry/imr-details/2380. Accessed January 13, 2022.

25. CT scan. Mayo Clinic. https://www.mayoclinic.org/tests-procedures/ct-scan/about/pac-20393675. Accessed January 18, 2022.

26. Boone JM, Hendee WR, McNitt-Gray MF, et al. Radiation exposure from CT scans: How to close our knowledge gaps, monitor and safeguard exposure-proceedings and recommendations of the radiation dose summit, sponsored by NIBIB. February 24-25, 2011. *Radiology*. 2012; 265(2):544-554. doi: 10.1148/radiol.12112201

27. Understanding radiation risk from imaging tests. American Cancer Society. https://www.cancer.org/treatment/understanding-your-diagnosis/tests/understanding-radiation-risk-from-imaging-tests.html. Accessed January 18, 2022.

28. Radiation doses. Canadian Nuclear Safety Commission. http://nuclearsafety.gc.ca/eng/resources/radiation/introduction-to-radiation/radiation-doses.cfm#fnb. Accessed January 20, 2022.

Notes

29. Personal annual radiation dose calculator. United States Regulatory Commission. https://www.nrc.gov/about-nrc/radiation/around-us/calculator.html. Accessed January 20, 2022.

30. Potential hazards and risks. UCSF Department of Radiology & Biomedical Imaging. https://radiology.ucsf.edu/patient-care/patient-safety/mri/potential-hazards-risks. Accessed January 18, 2022.

31. #61-Rajpaul Attariwala, M.D., Ph.D.: Cancer screening with full-Body MRI scans and a seminar on the field of radiology. Peter Attia, MD. https://peterattiamd.com/rajpaulattariwala/. Accessed January 20, 2022.

32. Bonhomme V, Staquet C, Montupil J, et al. General anesthesia: A probe to explore consciousness. *Front Sys Neurosci.* 2019;13(36) doi: 10.3389/fnsys.2019.00036

33. Hiramatsu Y. Basic standard procedure of abdominal hysterectomy: Part 1," *The Surgery Journal.* 2019;5(S 01):S2-S10. doi: 10.1055/s-0039-1678575

34. Surgery for ovarian cancer. American Cancer Society. https://www.cancer.org/cancer/ovarian-cancer/treating/surgery.html. Accessed January 21, 2022.

35. complete hysterectomy. Dictionary of Cancer Terms, National Cancer Institute. https://www.cancer.gov/publications/dictionaries/cancer-terms/def/complete-hysterectomy. Accessed January 15, 2022.

36. Ovarian cancer stages. American Cancer Society. https://www.cancer.org/cancer/ovarian-cancer/detection-diagnosis-staging/staging.html. Accessed January 20, 2022.

37. Longacre M, Ross E, Fang CY. Caregiving choice and emotional stress among cancer caregivers. *West J Nurs Res.*2013;36(6):806-824. doi: 10.1177/0193945913510211

38. Kim S. Caregivers' information overload and their personal health literacy. *West J Nurs Res.* 2021;43(5):431-441. doi: 10.1177/0193945920959086

39. Pereira MP, Wiegmann H, Agelopoulos K, et al. Neuropathic itch: Routes to clinical diagnosis. *Front Med.* 2021; 8:175. doi: 10.3389/fmed.2021.641746

40. Chan JK, Manetta A. Prevention of femoral nerve injuries in gynecological surgery. *Amer J Obstet Gynecol.* 2002;186(1):1-7. doi: 10.1067/mob.2002.119182

41. Irvin W, Anderson W, Taylor P, et al. Minimizing the risk of neurologic injury in gynecologic surgery. *Obstet Gynecol.* 2004;103(2): 374-82.

42. Rumsey N, Harcourt D. Body image and disfigurement: Issues and interventions. *Body Image.* 2004; 1(1): 83-97.

43. Food and Nutrition Board, Institute of Medicine. *Dietary Reference Intakes for Energy, Carbohydrate, Fiber, Fat, Fatty Acids, Cholesterol, Protein, and Amino Acids (Macronutrients).* National Academies Press; 2005: 589. https://www.nap.edu/read/10490/chapter/12. Accessed January 29, 2022.

44. Phillips SM, Chevalier S, Leidy HJ. Protein "requirements" beyond the RDA: Implications for optimizing health. *Appl Physiol Nutr Metab.* 2016;41(5):565-72. doi:10.1139/apnm-2015-0550

45. Manásek V, Bezdek K, Foltys A, et al. The impact of high protein nutritional support on clinical outcomes and treatment costs of patients. *Klinická Onkologie.* 2016;29(5):351-357. doi:10.14735/amko2016351

46. Digestive system. Cleveland Clinic. https://my.clevelandclinic.org/health/articles/7041-the-structure-and-function-of-the-digestive-system). Accessed January 31, 2022.

47. Sheth A and Richman J. *What's Your Poo Telling You?* Chronicle Books; 2007.

Notes

48. Bonaz B, Sinniger V, Pellissier S. Vagus nerve stimulation: A new promising therapeutic tool in inflammatory bowel disease. *J Intern Med*. 2017;281(1):46-63. doi: 10.1111/joim.12611

49. The dangers within: How blood clots affect your health. American Heart Association. https://www.heart.org/en/university-hospitals-harrington-heart-and-vascular/the-dangers-within-how-blood-clots-affect-your-health. Accessed on February 3, 2022.

50. Aidan JC, Priddee NR, McAleer JJ. Chemotherapy causes cancer! A case report of therapy related acute myeloid leukemia in early stage breast cancer. *Ulst Med J*. 2013;82(2):97-99.

51. Vega-Stromberg T. Chemotherapy-induced secondary malignancies. *J Infus Nurs*. 2003;26(6):353.

52. Boffetta P, Kaldor JM. Secondary malignancies following cancer chemotherapy. *Acta Oncologica*. 1994;33(6): 591-598.

53. Piccart MJ, Lamb H, Vermoken JB. Current and future potential roles of the platinum drugs in the treatment of ovarian cancer. *Ann Oncol*. 2001;12(9):1195-1203.

54. Kerr JFR, Winterford CM, Harmon BV. Apoptosis: Its significance in cancer and cancer therapy. *Cancer*. 2013;73(8):2013-2026.

55. Desai AG, Qazi GN, Ganju RK, et al. Medicinal plants and cancer chemoprevention. *Curr Drug Metab*. 2008;9(7):581-591.

56. Types of chemotherapy drugs. National Cancer Institute. https://training.seer.cancer.gov/treatment/chemotherapy/types.html. Accessed on February 5, 2022

57. Asher GN, Corbett AH, Hawke RL. Common herbal dietary supplement-drug interactions. *Am Fam Physician*. 2017,96(2):101-107.

58. About herbs, botanicals & other products. Memorial Sloan Kettering Cancer Center website. https://www.mskcc.org/ cancer-care/diagnosis-treatment/symptom-management/ integrative-medicine/herbs. Accessed February 6, 2022.

59. Dietary Supplement Fact Sheets. National Institutes of Health. https://ods.od.nih.gov/factsheets/list-all/. Accessed July 28, 2022.

60. Botanical Supplement Fact Sheets. National Institutes of Health. https://ods.od.nih.gov/factsheets/list-Botanicals/. Accessed July 28, 2022.

61. Vitamin and Mineral Supplement Fact Sheets. National Institutes of Health. https://ods.od.nih.gov/factsheets/list-VitaminsMinerals/. Accessed July 28, 2022.

62. How chemotherapy drugs work. American Cancer Society.https://www.cancer.org/content/dam/CRC/PDF/ Public/8418.00.pdf. Accessed February 5, 2022.

63. Espinosa E, Zamora P, Feliu J, et al. Classification of anticancer drugs-a new system based on therapeutic targets. *Cancer Treat Rev.* 2003;29(6):515-523. doi:10.1016/ S0305-7372(03)00116-6

64. How chemotherapy drugs work. American Cancer Society website. https://www.cancer.org/treatment/ treatments-and-side-effects/treatment-types/ chemotherapy/how-chemotherapy-drugs-work.html. Accessed February 5, 2022.

65. Reimer RR, Hoover R, Fraumeni JF, Young RC. Acute leukemia after alkylating-agent therapy of ovarian cancer. *N Engl J Med.* 1977;297(4):177-181. doi:10.1056/ NEJM19770728970402

66. Davies SM. Therapy-related leukemia associated with alkylating agents. *Med Pediatr Oncol.* 2001;36(5):536-540. doi:10.1002/mpo.1126

67 Park SB, Lin CSY, Krishnan AV, et al. Early, progressive, and sustained dysfunction of sensory axons underlies paclitaxel induced neuropathy. *Muscle Nerve.* 2011;43(3):367-374. doi:10.1002/mus.21874

68. Argyriou AA, Koltzenburg M, Polychronopoulos P, Papetropoulos S, Kalafonos HP. Peripheral nerve damage associated with administration of taxanes in patients with cancer. *Crit Rev Oncol Hemat.* 2008;66(3):218-228. doi:10.1016/j. critrevonc.2008.01.008

69. Surveillance, epidemiology, and end results program. National Cancer Institute. https://seer.cancer.gov/. Accessed on February 6, 2022.

70. Survival rates for ovarian cancer. American Cancer Society. https://www.cancer.org/cancer/ovarian-cancer/detection-diagnosis-staging/survival-rates.html. Accessed on February 6, 2022.

71. Hajar R. The physician's oath: Historical perspectives. *Heart Views.* 2017;18(4):154-159. doi: 10.4103/HEARTVIEWS.HEARTVIEWS_131_17

72. Longo VD, Mattson MP. Fasting: Molecular mechanisms and clinical applications. *Cell Metab.* 2046;19(2):181-192. doi: 10.1016/j.cmet.2013.12.008

73. Mattson MP, Longo VD, Harvie M. impact of intermittent fasting on health and disease processes. *Ageing Res Rev.* 2016;39:46-58. doi:10.1016/j.arr.2016.10.005

74. De Groot S, Lugtenberg RT, et al. Fasting mimicking diet as an adjunct to neoadjuvant chemotherapy for breast cancer in the multicentre randomized phase 2 DIRECT trial. *Nat Commun.* 2020;11(1):1-9. doi:10.1038/s41467-020-1138-3

75. Seyfried T. Cancer: a metabolic disease with metabolic solutions. Oral presentation at: Florida Institute for Human & Machine Cognition. March, 2015. Pensacola, FL.

76. Jones W, Bianchi K. Aerobic glycolysis: Beyond proliferation. *Front Immunol.* 2015;6:227.

77. Christofferson T. *Tripping Over the Truth: How the Metabolic Theory of Cancer Is Overturning One of Medicine's Entrenched Paradigms.* Chelsea Green; 2017.

78. Seyfried TN. *Cancer as a Metabolic Disease: On the Origin, Management and Prevention of Cancer.* John Wiley & Sons; 2012.

79. Seyfried TN. *Cancer as a Metabolic Disease: On the Origin, Management and Prevention of Cancer.* John Wiley & Sons; 2012.

80. Christofferson T. *Tripping Over the Truth: How the Metabolic Theory of Cancer Is Overturning One of Medicine's Entrenched Paradigms.* Chelsea Green; 2017.

81. Seyfried TN. Mitochondrial glutamine fermentation enhances ATP synthesis in murine glioblastoma cells. In: Proceedings of the 102nd Annual Meeting of the American Association for Cancer Research; 2011 Apr 2-6; Orlando, FL. Philadelphia (PA): AACR; Cancer Res 2011;71(8 Suppl):Abstract nr 985. doi:10.1158/1538-7445. AM2011-985

82. Seyfried TN, Marsh J, Shelton LM, et al. Is the restricted ketogenic diet a viable alternative to the standard of care for managing malignant brain cancer? *Epilepsy Res.* 2012;100(3):310-326. doi:10.1016/j.eplepsyres.2011.06.017

83. Seyfried TN, Shivane AG, Kalamian M, et al. Ketogenic metabolic therapy, without chemo or radiation, for the long-term management of IDH1-mutant glioblastoma: An 80-month follow-up case report. *Front Nutr.* 2021; 8:682243. doi:10.3389/fnut.2021.682243

84. Seyfried TN, Yu G, et al. Press-pulse:A novel therapeutic strategy for the metabolic management of cancer. *Nutr Metab.* 2017;14(1):1-17. doi:10.1186/s12986-017-0178-2

85. Arens NC, West ID. Press-pulse: A general theory of mass extinction? *Paleobiology.* 2008;34(4):456-471.

Notes

86. Tippens J. Get busy living. 2016. Available at: https://www.mycancerstory.rocks/. Accessed February 10, 2022.

87. Son DS, Lee ES, Adunyah SE. The antitumor potentials of benzimidazole anthelmintics as repurposing drugs. *Immune Net.* 2020;20(4): e29. doi:10.4110/in.2020.20.e29

88. Laudisi F, Marônek M, Di Grazia A, et al. Repositioning of anthelmintic drugs for the treatment of cancers of the digestive system. *Int J Mol Sci.* 2020; 21(14):4957. doi:10.3390/ijms21144957

89. Kunnumakkara AB, Bordloi D, Lalduhsaki Silo B, et al. Cancer drug development: The missing links. *Exp Biol Med.* 2019;244(8):663-689. doi:10.1177/1535370219839163

90. Sahragardjoonegani B, Beall RF, Kesselheim AS, et al. Repurposing existing drugs for new uses:A cohort study of the frequency of FDA-granted new indication exclusivities since 1997. *J Pharm Policy Pract.* 2021;14(1):1-8. doi:10.1186/s40545-020-00282-8

91. Gao P, Dang CV, Watson J. Unexpected antitumorigenic effect of fenbendazole when combined with supplementary vitamins. *J Am Assoc Lab Anim Sci.* 2008;47(6):37-40.

92. Chung I, Zhou K, Barrow C, et al. Unbiased phenotype-based screen identifies therapeutic agents selective for metastatic prostate cancer. *Front Oncol.* 2021;10:594141. doi:10.3389/fonc.2020.594141

93. Keystone JS, Murdoch JK. Drugs five years later: Mebendezole. *Annals of Internal Med.* 1979;91(4):582-586. doi:10.7326/0003-4819-91-4-582.

94. Canete R: A letter to the editor [Mebendezole is a potential alternative in the treatment of Giardia duodenalis infection]. *Curr Ther Res.* 2016; 80:1-2.

95. Seyfried TN, Sanderson TM, El-Abbadi MM, et al. Role of glucose and ketone bodies in the metabolic control of experimental brain cancer. *Br J Cancer.* 2003;89:1375-1382. doi:10.1038/sj.bjc.6601269

181

96. Peterman MG. The ketogenic diet in epilepsy. *JAMA.* 1925;84(26):1979-1983. doi:10.1001/jama.1925.02660520007003

97. Meidenbauer J, Mukherjee P, Seyfried TN. The glucose ketone index calculator: A simple tool to monitor therapeutic efficacy for metabolic management of brain cancer. *Nutr Metab.* 2015;12(1):1-7. doi:10.1186/s12986-015-0009-2

98. Data souces. Cronometer. https://support.cronometer.com/hc/en-us/articles/360018239472-Data-Sources. Accessed February 12, 2022.

99. What is a naturopathic doctor? American Association of Naturopathic Physicians. https://naturopathic.org/page/WhatisaNaturopathicDoctor. Accessed February 14, 2022.

100. Géry A, Dubreule C, André V, et al. Chaga (inonotus obliquus), a future potential medicinal fungus in oncology? A chemical study and a comparison of the cytoxicity against human lung adenocarcinoma cells (A549) and human bronchial epithelial cells (BEAS-2B). *Integr Cancer Ther.* 2018;17(3):832-843. doi:10.1177/153473541875912

101. Lee MG, Kwon YS, Nam KS, et al. Chaga mushroom extract induces autophagy via the AMPK-mTOR signaling pathway in breast cancer cells. *J Ethnopharmacol.* 2021;274:114081. doi:10.1016/j.jep.2021.114081

102. Glinsky VV, Raz A. Modified citrus pectin anti-metastatic properties: One bullet, multiple targets. *Carbohdyr Res.* 2009;344(14):1788-1791. doi:10.106/j.carres.2008.08.038

103. Pectin. Memorial Sloan Kettering Cancer Center. https://www.mskcc.org/cancer-care/integrative-medicine/herbs/pectin. Accessed on February 14, 2022.

104. Bushman JL. Green tea and cancer in humans: A review of the literature. *Nutr Cancer.* 1998;31(3):151-159. doi:10.1080/01635589809514697

Notes

105. Cheng Z, Zhang Z, Han Y, et al. A review of anti-cancer effect of green tea catechins. *J Funct Foods*. 2020;74:104172. doi:10.1016/j.jff.2020.104172

106. Du GJ, Zhang Z, Wen XD, et al. Epigallocatechin gallate (EGCG) is the most effective cancer chemoprotective polyphenol in green tea. *Nutrients*. 2012;4(11):1679-1691. doi:10.3390/nu4111679

107. Benzoni T, Hatcher JD. Bleach toxicity. *StatPearls [Internet]*. 2021.

108. Neag MA, Mocan A, Echeverria J, et al. Berberine: Botanical occurrence, traditional uses, extraction methods, and relevance in cardiovascular, metabolic, hepatic, and renal disorders. *Front Pharmacol*. 2018;9:557. doi:10.3389/fphar.2018.00557

109. Locke AB. Urinary tract infection (UTI). In: Rakel D, ed. *Integrative Medicine*. 4th ed. Elsevier; 2018: Chapter 23.

110. Wang Y, Liu Y, Du X, et al. The anti-cancer mechanisms of berberine: A review. *Cancer Manag Res*. 2020;12:695-702. doi:10.2147/CMAR.S242329

111. Jing Y, Kong WJ, J JD. Learning from berberine: Treating chronic diseases through multiple targets. *Science China Life Sciences*. 2015;58(9):854-859. doi:10.1007/s11427-013-4568-z

112. Mirhadi E, Rezaee M, Malaekah-Nikouei B. Nano strategies for berberine delivery, a natural alkaloid of Berberis. *Biomed Pharmacother*. 2018;104:465-473. doi:10.1016/j.biopha.2018.05.067

113. Unlu A, Nayir E, Kalenderoglu MD, et al. Curcumin (Turmeric) and cancer. *J Buon*. 2016;21(5):1050-1060.

114. Shoba G, Joy D, Joseph T, et al. Influence of piperine on the pharmacokinetics of curcumin in animals and human volunteers. *Planta Medica*. 1998;64(04):353-356.

115. Skeie G, Braaten T, Hjartaker A, et al. Cod liver oil, other dietary supplements and survival among cancer patients with solid tumours. *Int J Cancer*. 2009;125:1155-1160.

116. Dyck MC, Ma DWL, Meckling KA. The anticancer effects of vitamin D and omega-3 PUFAs in combination via cod liver oil: One plus one may equal more than two. *Med Hypotheses*. 2011;77(3):326-332.

117. Holick MF. Vitamin D deficiency. *N Engl J Med*. 2007;357:266-281

118. Alshahrani FM, Almalki MH, Aljohani N. Vitamin D light side and best time to sunshine in Riyadh, Saudi Arabia, *Dermato-Endocrinology*. 2013;5(1):177-170. doi:10.4161.derm.23351.

119. The seasons, the equinox, and the solstices. National Weather Service. https://www.weather.gov/cle/seasons. Accessed February 17, 2022.

120. NOAA solar calculator. Global Monitoring Laboratory Earth System Research Laboratories. https://gml.noaa.gov/grad/solcalc/index.html. Accessed on February 17, 2022.

121. Ultraviolet radiation. US Food & Drug Administration. https://www.fda.gov/radiation-emitting-products/tanning/ultraviolet-uv-radiation. Accessed February 17, 2022.

122. Holick MF. Vitamin D deficiency. *N Engl J Med*. 2007;357:266-281.

123. Alshahrani FM, Almalki MH, Aljohani N. Vitamin D light side and best time to sunshine in Riyadh, Saudi Arabia, *Dermato-Endocrinology*. 2013;5(1):177-170. doi:10.4161.derm.23351

124. Lucock M, Jones P, Martin C. Vitamin D: Beyond metabolism. *J Evid-Based Integr Med*. 2015;20(4):310-322. doi:10.1177/2156587215580491

125. Baggerly CA, Cuomo RE, French CB, et al. Sunlight and vitamin D: Necessary for public health. *J Amer Col Nutri*. 2015;34(4):359-365. doi:10.1080/07315724.2015.1039866

126. Erythropel HC, Maric M, Nicell JA, et al. Leaching of the plasticizer di (2-ethylhexyl) phthalate (DEHP) from plastic containers and the question of human exposure. *Appl Microbiol Biotechnol.* 2014;98(24):9967-9981. doi:10.1007/s00253-014-6183-8

127. Weiser R, Ross GL. The American Council on Science and Health. Teflon and Human Health: Do the Charges Stick? Assessing the Safety of PFOA. 2005.https://www.acsh.org/sites/default/files/teflon%20acsh%202005.pdf. Accessed February 17, 2022

128. Kamerud KL, Hobbie KA, Anderson KA. Stainless steels leaches nickel and chromium into foods during cooking. *J Agric Food Chem.* 2013;61(39):9495-9501. doi:10.1021/jf402400v

129. Quintaes KD, Amaya-Faran J, Tomazini FM, et al. Mineral migration and influence of meal preparation in iron cookware on the iron nutritional status of vegetarian students. *Ecol Food Nutr.* 2007;46(2):125-141. doi:10.1080/03670240701285079

130. Eating, diet, & nutrition for constipation. National Institute of Diabetes and Digestive and Kidney Diseases. https://www.niddk.nih.gov/health-information/digestive-diseases/constipation/eating-diet-nutrition. Accessed on February 19, 2022.

131. CA 125 test. Mayo Clinic. https://www.mayoclinic.org/tests-procedures/ca-125-test/about/pac-20393295. Accessed February 20, 2022.

132. The COC protocol in ovarian cancer. Care Oncology. https://careoncology.com/the-coc-protocol-in-ovarian-cancer/. Accessed on February 20, 2022.

133. Lee J, Hong EM, Jung JH, et al. Metformin induces apoptosis and inhibits proliferation through the AMP-activated protein kinase and insulin-like growth factor 1 receptor pathways in the bile duct cancer cells. *J Cancer.* 2019;10(7):1734-1744. doi:10.7150/jca.26380

WHOLE NEW ME

134. Lee JO, Kang MJ, Byun WS, et al. Metformin overcomes resistance to cisplatin in triple-negative breast cancer (TNBC) cells by targeting RAD51. *Breast Cancer Res.* 2019;21(1):1-18. doi:10.1186/s13058-019-1204-2

135. Martirosyan A, Clendening JW, Goard CA, et al. Lovastatin induces apoptosis of ovarian cancer cells and synergizes with doxorubicin: Potential therapeutic relevance. *BMC Cancer.* 2010;10(1):1-13. doi:10.1186/1471-2407-10-103

136. Vogel TJ, Goodman MT, Li AJ, et al. Statin treatment is associated with survival in a nationally representative population of elderly women with epithelial ovarian cancer. *Gynecol Oncol.* 2017;146(2):340-345. doi:10.1016/j.ygyno.2017.05.009

137. Nygren P, Larsson R. Drug repositioning from bench to bedside:Tumour remission by the antihelmintic drug mebendazole in refractory metastatic colon cancer. *Acta Oncologica.* 2014;53(3):427-428. doi:10.3109/0284186X.2013.844359

138. Nygren P, Fryknäs M, Ågerup B, et al. Repositioning of the anthelmintic drug mebendazole for the treatment for colon cancer. *J Can Res Clin Oncol.* 2013;139(12):2133-2140. doi:10.1007/s00432-013-1539-5

139. Guerini AE, Triggiani L, Maddalo M, et al. Mebendezole as a candidate for drug repurposing in oncology: An extensive review of current literature. *Cancers (Basel).* 2019;11(9):1284. doi:10.3390/cancers11091284

140. Sotgia F, Ozsvari B, Fiorillo M, et al. A mitochondrial based oncology platform for targeting cancer stem cells (CSCs):MITO-ONC-RX. *Cell Cycle.* 2018;17(17):2091-2100. doi:10.3389/fonc.2018.00452

141. Roomi MW, Monterrey JC, Kalinovsky T, et al. In vitro modulation of MMP-2 and MMP-9 in human cervical and ovarian cancer cell lines by cytokines, inducers and inhibitors. *Oncol Rep.* 2010;23(3):605-614. doi:10.3892/or_00000675

142. The COC Protocol in Ovarian Cancer. https://careoncology.com/the-coc-protocol-in-ovarian-cancer/. Accessed July 16, 2022.

143. Protocol. Cellcore Biosciences. https://cellcore.com/pages/protocol. Accessed June 18, 2022.

144. Cellcore Biosciences-UNPARALLELED Detoxification. Dr. Davidson & Dr. Mullins discuss products. https://www.youtube.com/watch?v=zp2b9ozUUsl. Accessed June 18, 2022.

CHAPTER 2: THE MIND

1. Harrigan JS. Kundalini Vidya *The Science of Spiritual Transformation: A Comprehensive System for Understanding and Guiding Spiritual Development.* Patanjali Kundalini Yoga Care; 2006.

2. Home, PKYC Patanjali Kundalini Yoga Care. http://www.kundalini-science.ch/. Accessed May 11, 2022.

3. Stevensen, I. *Children Who Remember Previous Lives.* McFarland & Company; 2000.

4. Haraldsson E. A psychological comparison between ordinary children and those who claim previous-life memories. *J Sci Explor.* 1997;1(3):323-335.

5. Garfield JL. What is it like to be a boddhisattva? Moral phenomenology in Śāntideva's Bodhicaryāvatāra. *JIABS.* 2010;33(1-2):333-357.

6. Park IH, Cho LJ. Confucianism and the Korean family. *J Comp Fam Stud.* 1995;26(1):117-134.

7. Palais J. Confucianism and the aristocratic/bureaucratic balance in Korea. *Harv J Asiat Stud.* 1984;44(2): 427-468.

CHAPTER 3: THE SPIRIT

1. Gupta R, Valpey K. *The Bhagavata Purana: Sacred Text and Living Tradition.* Columbia University Press; 2013.
2. Rumi, JA, Barks C, Green M. *The Illuminated Rumi.* Broadway Books; 1997.
3. Moorjani, A. *Dying to Be Me.* Hay House; 2014.
4. Eadie BJ. *Embraced By the Light: The Most Profound and Complete Near-Death Experience Ever.* Golden Leaf Press; 1992.
5. Diamond D. *Life After Near Death: Miraculous Stories of Healing and Transformation in the Extraordinary Lives of People with Newfound Powers.* New Page Books; 2016.

CONCLUSION

1. Thakar R, Manyoda I, Stanton L, Clarkson P, Robindon G. Bowel function and hysterectomy - A review. *Int Urogynecol J.* 2001;12: 337-341.
2. Thakar R, Manyoda I, Stanton L, Clarkson P, Robindon G. Bowel function and hysterectomy - A review. *Int Urogynecol J.* 2001;12: 337-341.
3. Kocaay AF, Oztuna D, Su FA, Elhan AH, Kuzu MA. Effects of hysterectomy on pelvic floor disorders: a longitudinal study. *Dis Colon Rectum.* 2017;60(3):303-310. doi: 10.1097/DCR.0000000000000786

4. Martinelli E, Altomare DF, Rinaldi M, Portincasa P. Constipation after hysterectomy: Fact or fiction? *Eur J Surg.* 2000;166(5): 356-560.

5. Kelly J, O'Riordain D, Jones E. et al. The effect of hysterectomy on ano-rectal physiology. *Int J Colorect Dis.* 1998;13: 116–118. https://doi.org/10.1007/s003840050147

6. Sontag S. *Illness as Metaphor.* Farrar, Straus, Giroux; 1978.

7. Clow, B. Who's afraid of Susan Sontag? or, the myths and metaphors of cancer reconsidered. *Society Soc Hist Med.* 2001;14(2): 293-312.

8. Seyfried TN, Shelton LM. Cancer as a metabolic disease. *Nutr Metab.* 2010;7(1): 1-22. doi: 10.1186/1743-7075-7-7.

APPENDIX A: THE MANIFESTATION PROCESS AND THE EVOLUTION OF THE MIND

1. Niranjanananda Saraswati S. *Samkhya Darhsan/Yogic Perspective on Theories of Realism.* Yoga Publications Trust; 2008.

2. Virupakshananda S. *Samkhya Karika of Isvara Krsna with the Ttatva Kaumudi of Sri Vacaspati Misra.* Sri Ramakrishna Math; 1995.

3. Schweizer P. Mind consciousness dualism in Sankhya-Yoga Philosophy. *Philos Phenomenol Res.* 1993;53(4): 845-859.

4. Niranjanananda Saraswati S. *Samkhya Darhsan/Yogic Perspective on Theories of Realism.* Yoga Publications Trust; 2008.

5. Lad V. *Textbook of Ayurveda: Fundamental Principles of Ayurveda Volume One.* Ayurvedic Press; 2002.

6. Lad V. *Textbook of Ayurveda: Fundamental Principles of Ayurveda Volume One.* Ayurvedic Press; 2002.

7. Moorjani, A. *Dying to Be Me.* Hay House; 2014.

8. Turner, K. *Radical Remission: Surviving Cancer Against All Odds.* Harper One; 2014.

APPENDIX B: MODES OF THE MIND

1. Hariharānanda Arānya S. *Yoga Philosophy of Patanjali.* SUNY; 1983.

APPENDIX C: KARMA

1. Chakraborty P. The law of karma and salvation. *Intl J Hum Soc Sci Stud.* 2014;1(3):193-195.

2. Chakraborty P. The law of karma and salvation. *Intl J Hum Soc Sci Stud.* 2014;1(3):193-195.

3. Kachhara NL, Tater SR, Pragya SU. *Karma, living system, genes and human performance. Scientific Perspectives of Jainism.* 2017: 115-149.

4. Hariharānanda Arānya S. *Yoga Philosophy of Patanjali.* SUNY; 1983.

APPENDIX D: INTUITION

1. intuition (noun), Merriam-Webster. https://www.merriam-webster.com/dictionary/intuition. Accessed April 23, 2022.

2. MacLean PD. *The Triune Brain in Evolution: Role in Paleocerebral Functions.* Plenum; 1990.

3. Pessoa L. Understanding brain networks and brain organization. *Phys Life Rev.* 2014. 11(3): 400-435. doi: 10.1016/j.plrev.2014.03.005

Notes

4. Power JD, Fair DA, Schlaggar BL, Petersen SE. The development of human functional brain networks. *Neuron.* 201;67(5): 735-748. doi: 10.1016/j.neuron.2010.08.017

5. Raichle ME. The brain's default mode network. *Annu Rev Neurosci.* 2015;38: 433-447. doi: 10.1146/annurev-neuro-071013-014030

6. Tripathi V, Bharadwaj P. Neuroscience of the yogic theory of consciousness. *Neurosci Conscious.* 2021;7(2): 1-15. doi:10.1093/nc/niab030

7. Furness JB. The enteric nervous system and neurogastroenterology. *Nat Rev Gastroenterol Hepatol.* 2012;9(5): 286-294. doi: 10.1038/nrgastro.2012.32

8. Mayer EA. Gut feelings: The emerging biology of gut-brain communication. *Nat Rev Neurosci.* 2011;12(8): 453-466. doi:10.1038/nrn3071

9. Van Oudenhove L, Lukas SM, Lassman DJ, et al. Emotional modulation of fatty acid induced gut-brain signaling in brainstem, subcortical and cortical regions: An fMRI study. *Gastroenterol.* 2010;138(5): S-45. doi: 10.1016/S0016-5085(10)60205-3

10. Jiang H, Betancourt L, Smith RG. Ghrelin amplifies dopamine signaling by cross talk involving formation of growth hormone secretagogue receptor/dopamine receptor subtype 1 heterodimers. *Mol Endocrinol.* 2006;20(8): 1772–1785. doi: 10.1210/me.2005-0084

11. Preuschoff K, Quartz SR, Bossaerts P. Human insula activation reflects risk prediction errors as well as risk. *J Neurosci.* 2008;12(28): 2745-52. doi: 10.1523/JNEUROSCI.4286-07.2008.

12. Prinz J. Are emotions feelings? *J Conscious Stud.* 2005;12(8-9): 9-25.

13. Dörfler V, Ackerman F. Understanding intuition: The case for two forms of intuition. *Manag Learn.* 2012;43(5):545-564. doi:10.1177/1350507611434686

APPENDIX E: FIVE SHEATHS OF HUMAN EXISTENCE

1. Niranjanananda S. *Samkhya Darhsan/Yogic Perspective on Theories of Realism*. Yoga Publications Trust; 2008.

2. Sivananda S. *The Principal Upanishads*. 5th ed. The Divine Life Society; 2008.

3. Jha M. Personality: A yogic conception. *Ind J Soc Sci Research*. 2009;6(1): 39-45.

About the Author

Angie N. Choi, EdD, is the Director of Admissions and Assistant Professor at the University of Arkansas for Medical Sciences in the College of Pharmacy. She holds a doctorate in higher education and a master's degree in Asian philosophies and religion. She is also certified as a hypnotist and yoga teacher. She has studied eastern and western ideas about consciousness and the mind and is interested in helping others become more self-aware. Dr. Choi is also the author of *My Dreams: A Simple Guide to Dream Interpretation*. Dr. Choi enjoys sharing knowledge, public speaking, writing poetry, taking walks, contemplation, and living simply.

Dear Reader,

It was my sincere aspiration to provide a cancer memoir of integrated healing in body, mind, and spirit. The body, mind, and spirit work together to heal and can help us through the most difficult ordeals. I wanted to offer hope to anyone who hears, "You have cancer." There are many people who survive cancer and find the way out of darkness toward the light.

Given my inspiration for this book, was this book helpful? I'd love to hear your suggestions for improving any future editions at info@kosmospublications.com. Also, if you purchased this book online, please take a few minutes to leave a review of this book. I would be extremely grateful and will read all the comments and suggestions.

Sincerely,
Angie N. Choi